SICK CAESARS

SICK CAESARS

SICK CAESARS

MICHAEL GRANT

BARNES
&NOBLE
B O O K S
N E W   Y O R K

2000 Barnes & Noble Books

ISBN 0-7607-0937-8

Text design by Catherine Schurdak

Printed and bound in the United States of America

00   01   02   03   04   MC   9   8   7   6   5   4   3   2   1

QF

CONTENTS

LIST *of* ILLUSTRATIONS

LIST *of* MAPS

INTRODUCTION

Historians and doctors, rightly said F. F. Cartwright,[1]

have much in common. Both acknowledge that the
proper study of mankind is Man. Both are particularly interested in the influences which condition human existence. . . . Particularly at a time when the sociological
aspects of history are being emphasised, it is worth ex-
amining those episodes in which the influence of disease
may have been of real importance, especially when that
importance has been neglected or misconstrued by more
conventional historians. . . . The various maladies which
have afflicted the world . . . [have exercised] their effect
not only upon historically important individuals, but also
upon the peoples. Thus the study is relevant to History,
whether conceived as a saga of great figures or as the story
of social conditions and general human development.

The Caesars ruled a gigantic part of the known world. They
were therefore of very great importance, an importance which can be

well judged today, when the tendency once again is for units to become blended into huge divisions of the globe.

It is strange, therefore, to discover that many of the Caesars were in poor states of health. This applies, for example, to Julius Caesar, Augustus, Tiberius, Gaius (Caligula), Claudius, Galba, Domitian, Marcus Aurelius, Commodus, Septimius Severus, Caracalla, Elagabalus, Diocletian and Constantine the Great—who, between them, ruled the empire during vast periods: and other emperors, too, were struck down by illness, and died, while relatively young. Since the doings of all these emperors tend to be little known or forgotten, the present book will outline their lives and careers, before discussing their health.[2]

The nature of the ill-health from which many of the rulers suffered is often obscure. That is partly because ancient illnesses were not always similar to modern ones, but there are other reasons as well. An effort will be made in this book to find out what was really wrong with each of them in turn, or in any case to record the symptoms of their illnesses. In the course of this discussion consideration will be given to the question whether, for example, epilepsy and gout were exactly what we would suppose them to be nowadays. It will also be necessary to assess the differences between being bad, ill or mad: a matter which is of profound concern to judges today, and greatly affects the sentences which they hand out.

This question of the rulers' health was by no means a trivial one, of secondary importance. On the contrary, their ill-health greatly influenced the course of major events, as will be duly pointed out. Moreover, some rulers utilised the precarious state of their health quite deliberately, and precisely in order to influence what happened.

Several things have to be remembered about the Caesars. First, they were monarchs of all they surveyed; over the whole gigantic area that has been mentioned. Nobody could criticise them, and get away with it; they could do what they liked. This is worth bearing in mind. Whom do you know who would behave really decently in such a situation, if it could ever exist? Or would you behave decently yourself? Just think: if one had all that power, what would one do, or not do? When one considers the failings of the Roman Caesars, let us remember what their position was. Let us, indeed, make allowances for them: if that is the right word. Or at any rate let us recognise how untrammelled their position was, and let us try to understand them in this context.

Secondly, we have to bear in mind that because of the greatness of their power they were extremely liable to conspiracies and attacks. Many other people wanted their extraordinary position, and the way to secure it was by murdering their incumbent, and taking his place. So it is hardly surprising that the daily lives of the Caesars, and their activities and behaviour, were dominated by the fear of plots—that is to say, by emotional fear and suspicion. The emperor Domitian is quoted as making a very sensible remark about this: 'the lot of emperors' (he is reported to have said, and it is probable enough that he did so—and that other rulers had made similar observations previously) 'is necessarily wretched, since only their assassination can convince the public that the conspiracies against their lives are real.'[3] And real they were, and real the Caesars understandably, and correctly, believed them to be.

Besides, the Caesars were, as will be suggested, a pretty odd lot. Reference has been made by others to their mixture of tastes: a passion for vulgar activities, combined with a lively interest in intellectual matters. Many of them considered themselves practically gods; but at the same time they were often practically fiends.[4] Although we really do not know much about them: we were not in, or near, the palace.

As has been mentioned, they often suffered from ill-health. This was sometimes physical, and sometimes mental. Doctors were not very good,[5] and the peculiarities of these imperial patients burgeoned. Sometimes they were peculiarities shared by large numbers of their peoples; sometimes instead they were forms of ill-health—health more or less peculiar to themselves, or at least developed by themselves to an extraordinary degree.[6]

There has been a good deal of modern literature about the illnesses of people in power. I am grateful to Dr. Frank MacMurray for letting me know about some of this. I also owe a debt of thanks to Mr. Stuart Miller and Ms. Carol Kelly-Gangi, of Barnes & Noble, for their helpfulness about the book, and, as always, I want to acknowledge my wife's frequent assistance.

—Michael Grant
Gattaiola, Italy
1999

SICK CAESARS

CHAPTER I

JULIUS CAESAR

JULIUS CAESAR HAS THE REPUTATION OF HAVING BEEN ONE OF THE greatest people who have ever lived. He was born in 100 BC, the son of Gaius Caesar (who died in about 85 without becoming consul); and his mother was Aurelia, of the distinguished Cotta family. His father's sister had become the wife of Marius. He himself, in 84, married Cornelia, daughter of Marius's ally against Sulla, Cinna. He served as a young man in Asia (81); and in 77 he unsuccessfully prosecuted Dolabella (consul 81) and Gaius Antonius. Then he retired to Rhodes for purposes of study, but fought against the pirates (75–74). In Rome he became *pontifex* (priest), and supported Pompey. Then in 68, Cornelia being dead, he remarried Pompeia—who was the grand-daughter of Sulla—but during his expensive aedileship of 63 (which was probably financed by Crassus) he restored the trophies of Sulla's enemy Marius.

In 63 he was elected *pontifex maximus* (chief priest), and after numerous vicissitudes divorced Pompeia—because 'his family must be above suspicion'. He then married Calpurnia. He claimed a triumph for alleged victories in Further Spain, but without success. In 59 he formed a close compact with Pompey and Crassus, the First

Triumvirate, which controlled the Roman world. Then Caesar received Cisalpine Gaul and Illyricum as a province for five years, and the Senate added Transalpine Gaul. From 58 to 51 Caesar commanded the Roman army in the Gallic Wars (which included invasions of Britain in 55 and 54), and the Triumvirate was prevented from falling apart by the Conference of Lucca between its leaders in 56. But Pompey's wife and Caesar's daughter Julia died in 54, and Crassus was killed by the Parthians in 53. Civil war with Pompey and his sons followed: on January 1st 49 Caesar crossed the Rubicon. He beat Pompey's lieutenants at Ilerda (Lerida) in Spain (40) and Pompey himself at Pharsalus in Thessaly (August 48); Pompey died in Egypt, where Caesar became the lover of Cleopatra VII (now queen). He then defeated Pharnaces II, king of the (Cimmerian) Bosphorus (Crimea) at Zela (Zile), and Pompey's general Scipio at Thapsus (Ed Dimas) in north Africa (46). Then he wound up the war by defeating Pompey's sons at Munda in southern Spain (March 45).

On returning from Ilerda Caesar was made dictator (to conduct elections), and reappointed in 48. In 46 he was granted the dictatorship for ten years, and in 44 for life. His head appeared on coins of 45–44. He was assassinated on March 15, 44.

He was a man of extremely clear vision and astonishing versatility. He was an extraordinarily able general. With him the Roman Republic unmistakably came to an end.

On the whole, despite his incessant activity Caesar's health was not too bad—and certainly did not impair his energy. Yet we cannot sum up his condition with any confidence, apart from suggesting that he became somewhat deaf at a comparatively early age,

'A particularly competent modern physician', wrote Gelzer, 'who thoroughly investigated the evidence about Caesar's illness and came to the conclusion that it was doubtful whether a diagnosis could be made after two thousand years.'[1]

In ancient times, however, it was said that Caesar's illness was epilepsy, and this may very well have been the case, although if so he clearly did not experience the more serious forms of that illness. In other words, if epilepsy was his trouble, he suffered not from the *grand mal,* which involves convulsions, but from the *petit mal,* which causes momentary loss of consciousness without convulsive movements. It is possible, but not certain, that he inherited this condition, which apparently characterised some of his ancestors, and was something of a family complaint. Caesar could not stand alcohol, which is characteristic of epileptics.

We have no evidence of Caesar suffering from any such troubles when he was young. But Plutarch mentions a fainting fit at Corduba (Cordova) in 49 BC, which was presumably epileptic. And then Caesar had another attack at Thapsus, in north Africa. This is what Plutarch wrote on the subject:

> So far from making his poor health an excuse for living an easy life, he used warfare as a tonic for his health. By long, hard journeys, simple diet, sleeping night after night in the open, he fought off his illness and made his body strong enough to resist all attacks.

Plutarch knew of other sources according to which Caesar took no part in the battle [of Thapsus]. 'While he was drawing up his army in battle order he is said to have been overcome by his usual sickness.' He reportedly felt an attack coming on and had himself carried away. The 'usual sickness' was epilepsy, from which various sources say he suffered. We have evidence of other sudden attacks. . . . An epileptic attack might explain why Caesar lost control of the army at Thapsus.[2]

Certainly Caesar had, for a Roman, a remarkably pale complexion, but there must, however, remain in the mind some doubt as to whether he did not utilise his illness for political purposes.[3] The battle was against Pompey's sons—part of the Civil War—and it was clearly undesirable to kill too many Romans, as the ancient writers were ready to emphasise.[4] It was therefore not altogether inconvenient that the massacre of fellow-Romans that followed, even if he himself (though not the orderer) was eventually to blame, could be dissociated from his name and authorship.

This was particularly possible because of the special reputation of epilepsy. To the Greeks it was *the* sacred disease: it is the only disease which the Hippocratic writings ascribe to a divine origin. Moreover, the Romans gave it (and Caesar's illness) especial respect and venerability as the *morbus comitialis*—an attack of which postponed elections and other public business. Nor was Caesar the first, if indeed he did so, to feign a seizure for political reasons. As for the public, they were perfectly ready, for the most part, to identify epilepsy with divine possession, and that is the feeling from which Caesar may well have benefited.[5]

During his last years Caesar, who had always driven himself desperately hard, suffered from headaches and fainting fits. Towards the end, an unpleasant incident occurred, which Caesar explained on the grounds, not entirely accepted by many, of quite another sort of illness, namely diarrhoea.

The situation was that he became the recipient of a great many official distinctions. We need not doubt that these were voted to him, because coins of the period display his portrait with the quasi-monarchic and contradictory inscription DICTATOR PERPETVO: the dictatorship was supposed to be only temporary, to deal with a crisis, and Caesar's acceptance of it in perpetuity was a sort of substitute for regal, autocratic titles.[6]

This was Dio's account:

When once they had voted to him on a single day an unusual number of these honours of especial importance . . . they then approached him as he was sitting in the vestibule of the Temple of Venus in order to announce to him in a body their decisions. . . . And either by some heaven-sent fatuity or through excess of joy he received them sitting, which aroused so great indignation among them all, not only the senators but all the rest, that it afforded his slayers one of the chief excuses for their plot against him. Some who subsequently tried to defend him claimed, it is true, that owing to an attack of diarrhoea he could not control the movement of his bowels and so had remained

where he was to avoid a flux. They were not able, however, to convince the majority, since not long afterwards he rose up and went home on foot.[7]

Suetonius gives some further details of what was evidently
built up as a major criticism:

> What made the Romans hate him so bitterly was that
> when, one day, the entire senate, armed with an im-
> posing list of honours that they had just voted him,
> came to where he sat in front of the Temple of Mother
> Venus, he did not rise to greet them. According to
> some accounts he would have risen had not Cornelius
> Balbus prevented him: according to others, he made
> no such move and grimaced angrily at Gaius Tre-
> batius, who suggested this courtesy.[8]

That said Suetonius, who was clearly unwilling to take account of Caesar's incessant and psychological strain, was an insult
which clearly showed his contempt for the Senate. This is how
Gelzer saw the incident:

> All the magistrates, with the consuls at their head, fol-
> lowed by the whole Senate, made their way to Caesar
> who was on a visit to his newly established Forum.
> They found him sitting in front of the temple of Venus
> Genetrix, and it was thus, without rising, that he re-

ceived the most distinguished body in Rome when it appeared before him with its solemn pronouncement. Perhaps he was attempting thereby to express the fact that the sovereign authority with which he had gradually been entrusted, even to the extent of full recognition of the divinity which was manifesting itself in him, extended over all subjects of whatever rank. But this behaviour was unfavourably received both by the participant senators and by the watching multitude, and he thought it advisable to spread it around that he had been seized by a sudden physical infirmity.[9]

And this was Plutarch's line:

[He remained seated when a delegation came to award him honours.] Later, however, he excused his behaviour on account of his illness, saying that those who suffer from it are apt to lose control of their senses if they address a large crowd while standing; in these circumstances they are very subject to fits of giddiness and may fall into convulsions and insensibility. This excuse, however, was not true.[10]

And it is Plutarch who brings in the reference to Cornelius Balbus. 'Remember,' Balbus is said to have observed, 'that you are Caesar. You are their superior and ought to let them treat you as such.'[11] Which is what, apparently, Caesar did.

According to Walter, Plutarch meant that Caesar was afraid he was going to have an epileptic fit; this is contradicted by Dio, but I am sure Walter was right to suppose that Caesar feared he would be assassinated—as he was. Walter also suggests that he acted as he did out of revenge for an insult that he had recently received from the tribune Aquila. This is uncertain, but it seems incontestable that he wanted to emphasise his supreme position, and only later, when he saw how badly this had gone down, utilised ill-health as an explanation and justification of his behaviour.[12]

For Caesar was no longer willing to show any consideration, and despite his immense physical strength his powers were failing— he had lived very hard, and now he sometimes found it difficult to control himself:[13] as early as 46 he concluded that he had lived long enough for himself and his fame, and seems to have been possessed by a kind of fatality.[14]

> His health was beginning to decline. His stomach troubled him. His epileptic fits were becoming more frequent and more serious. Physically, he was very weary. His words to the Senate, '*I have lived enough*', were not a mere affectation on his part. They were the result of a long physiological process that had been going on secretly and imperceptibly during the years of political struggle and military battles. . . . He re- alised with consternation that since he had given up his restless camp life and returned to the ordered exis- tence of a city dweller [his health] had constantly de-

teriorated and his attacks of epilepsy were becoming more and more frequent. He could not resign himself to the fact that this progressive weakening of his constitution was the inevitable result of advancing years; he imagined . . . that an active out-of-door life agreed with him better than the sedentary existence of cities. . . . Suetonius puts forward this curious explanation: 'Some of his relatives had the impression that he no longer cared to live and looked with indifference upon his declining health; it was, in their view, for this reason that he spurned the religious auguries and the admonitions of his friends.' But in that case how shall we explain the grandiose schemes which he was nourishing precisely at this period?[15]

This incident just discussed has been considered one of the reasons why he was murdered soon afterwards, but another was his decision to go east, lead the armies, and become a second Alexander, leaving the control of Rome to his henchmen, of whom the Senate took a poor view: Cicero wrote that 'he would never have returned from the Parthian War'.

Caesar's was a remarkable career. He is one of the most successful men who have ever lived, and he achieved what he achieved by constant hard work, despite onsets of ill-health. One wonders what he might have achieved if he had not suffered from these. One thing which he conspicuously failed to achieve was the establishment of the Roman principate. He lived while the Republic was collapsing, and he played his part in that collapse and indeed completed it. But it was left to Augustus to establish an imperial regime in its place. If Caesar had had better health, could he have done so? We cannot tell, but at least we can conclude that towards the end of his fifty-six years of life his health was failing, so it remains doubtful whether he could have done much more.

CHAPTER II

AUGUSTUS

Augustus was born in 63 BC and died in AD 14. He was the founder of the Roman principate, the imperial system which for centuries governed the huge empire. His real, original name was Gaius Octavius. His father, of that name, died in 59 BC, and he was brought up by his mother Atia, the niece of Julius Caesar, who introduced him to Roman life. At the age of twelve, he pronounced the tribute *(laudatio)* of his dead grandmother Julia. He was appointed *pontifex* (priest), and in 46 accompanied his great-uncle Julius Caesar in his triumph. He joined him in Spain in 45, and was at Apollonia, completing his studies with Agrippa, when he learnt of Caesar's death. The opening of Caesar's will revealed that Octavian had been adopted and made his chief heir, taking the name of Gaius Julius Caesar Octavianus. He soon reached a compromise agreement with Antony and Lepidus, and the Lex Titia gave them supreme authority as triumvirs (the Second Triumvirate), in which capacity the young man behaved cruelly. He strengthened his control of Italy and Gaul, and in 37 at Tarentum he and Antony had their powers extended for five years. In 36 Pompey's son, Sextus Pompeius, was defeated, and between 35 and 33 Octavian campaigned in Illyricum and Dalmatia. Relations with Antony (Lepidus having been extruded into the post of high priest) broke down, and Octavian defeated him at Actium (31) and seized Egypt (30). Consul since 30, in 27 he received the name Augustus and many honours. Campaigns and crises followed, and 23 witnessed the end of the Republic. In 22–19 BC Augustus travelled in Sicily, Greece and Parthia, which recognised the Roman protectorate in Armenia. In 17 he adopted his grandsons Gaius and Lucius, in 16–15 Raetia and Noricum were annexed as provinces, and for three years (15–13) Augustus resided in Gaul. The death of Lepidus made it possible for Augustus to replace him as high priest (12), and the death of Agrippa resulted in military activity by Tiberius and Drusus the elder.

But in 6 BC Tiberius retired to Rhodes through jealousy of Gaius. However, the death of Gaius in AD 4, following that of his brother Lucius in AD 2, resulted in the adoption of Tiberius. In AD 6 Judaea was annexed as a province, but a rebellion in Pannonia revealed the weakness of the Roman army, which was further underlined by Varus's loss of three legions at the Teutoburg Forest in AD 9, a loss that caused Augustus to abandon Germany and retain only twenty-five legions. In 13 he deposited his will in the House of the Vestals at Rome, and with it the *Monumentum Ancyranum,* or *Res Gestae,* his autobiographical record. In 14 he died at Nola, and was made a god of the state by the Senate. Augustus had the talent and good fortune to enrol Virgil, Horace and Livy as supporters of his cause.

This was Suetonius's account:

His body is said to have been marred by blemishes of various sorts—a constellation of seven birth-marks on his chest and stomach, exactly corresponding in form, order and number with the Great Bear; and a number of hard, dry patches suggesting ringworm, caused by an itching of his skin and a too frequent and vigorous use of the scraper at the Baths. He had a weakness in his left hip, thigh and leg, which occasionally gave him the suspicion of a limp; but this was improved by the sand-and-reed treatment. Sometimes the forefinger of his right hand would be so numbed and shrunken by cold that it hardly served to guide a pen, even when strengthened with a horn finger-stall. He also suffered from bladder-pains which, however, ceased to trouble him once he had passed gravel in his urine. He was subject to certain disorders which recurred every year; in early spring a tightness of the diaphragm; and when the sirocco blew, catarrh. These so weakened his constitution that either hot or cold weather caused him great distress.[1]

This is how Firth summed up his health:

Augustus was never physically strong. . . . He had many long and dangerous illnesses; and was constantly troubled with stone and a disordered liver. Every spring he used to complain of a swelling in the region

of his heart, while, when the south winds were preva-
lent, he was never free from catarrh. The extremes
both of heat and cold tried him severely. . . . He was a
confirmed valetudinarian, and preferred being rubbed
with oil to washing in cold water, and frequently used
sea water or warm sulphur water as a tonic.[2]

Massie wrote as follows:

His health, which had been poor in his youth, improved as he grew older. All the same, he had to take
care of himself. He disliked extremes of temperature,
wearing as many as four tunics, and a heavy woollen
gown and woollen underpants in winter, and always a
broad-brimmed straw hat to protect himself from the
sun. He suffered from catarrh when the sirocco (that
harsh south wind that is the curse of the Roman climate) was blowing.

So Augustus suffered from continuous bad health,
and it is quite remarkable that he lived a very long life,
for a Roman, in spite of constant illnesses. 'Some modern historians', we are told, 'consider Augustus harder
to understand than any other historical figure.' And
part of the reason is that he achieved such an immense
amount despite ill-health. As Arnaldo Momigliano
imaginatively quoted him as saying, this started very
early: 'I spent my youth sneezing and expectorating,

coughing, wheezing like a pair of holed bellows, shiv-
ering with agues, sweating with fever, stricken by migraine, oppressed by bile, frequently unable to sit a
horse or carry on a conversation that wasn't inter-
rupted by nose-blowing, nose-bleeds or nausea. . . . I
spent my first three weeks as consul with Caesar with
a tortured throat, a runny nose, spots before the eyes
and a high temperature. I was working eighteen hours
a day.'[3]

For the trouble was that, as has already been suggested, Augustus was not physically strong.

Augustus suffered several grave and dangerous illnesses at different periods. The worst was after his
Cantabrian conquest, when abscesses on the liver re-
duced him to such despair that he consented to try a
remedy which ran counter to all medical practice: because hot fomentations afforded him no relief, his
physician Antonius Musa successfully presented cold
ones. He was also subject to certain seasonal disorders
which recurred every year: in early spring a tightness
of the diaphragm; and when the sirocco blew, catarrh.
These so weakened his constitution that either hot or
cold weather caused him great distress . . . hot brine or
warm Albulan water was prescribed for his rheumatism.[4]

At the risk of repetition, let us hear how Firth summed the matter up:

> His left hip and leg were weak and made him walk rather lame, and the index finger of his right hand was subject to cramp which necessitated his wearing a horn ring for its support when he wrote. He had many long and dangerous illnesses; and was constantly troubled with stone and a disordered liver. Every spring he used to complain of a swelling in the region of his heart, while, when the south winds were prevalent, he was never free from catarrh. The extremes both of heat and cold tried him severely . . . . He was a confirmed valetudinarian. . . . In later life he travelled in a litter, usually at night . . . at a snail's pace.[5]

Thus not long after the death of Caesar, when Octavian (the future Augustus) was allied with Antony to defeat Caesar's assassins Brutus and Cassius, Octavian missed both battles of Philippi (42 BC) because he was unwell—a fact which Antony did not fail to stress to the public when he and his former ally were at variance later on.

As I wrote in *The Twelve Caesars:*

> Missing battles owing to bad health became, for Augustus, a recurrent pattern, which raises difficult questions about the possibly psychosomatic origins of

certain of his illnesses. Why, for example, when he and
Antony were confronting Brutus and Cassius at
Philippi (42 BC), was he not present at the first battle
at all? His own explanation was that he decided to
withdraw when the fighting started because his medical adviser had dreamt an ill-omened dream.[6] According to another account, the dream had urged him to
get up from his sick-bed and make a quick getaway
before the victorious enemy sacked his camp. In any
case, even his friends did not deny that he went and
hid in a marsh. Furthermore, he was ill on the occasion
of the Second Battle of Philippi as well. When both
battles were finished and won, it was scarcely surprising to find that Antony, in the subsequent division of
the Roman empire, emerged as very much the senior
partner.

Octavian's life, it was said, was only saved at
Philippi because his doctor Artorius, inspired (it was
said) by a dream, insisted that he should place himself in the front line. The physician who attended
Caesar [Octavian] dreamt that Minerva commanded
him to lead his patient, though still in poor health,
from his tent and place him in the line of battle—
the very means by which he was actually saved.
For . . . it was very manifestly the result of his leaving the entrenchments and mingling with the com-
batants that he survived, although by reason of his

sickness he found it difficult to stand even without his arms.[7]

Later on, the same sort of pattern manifested itself:

Octavian's continued ill-health flattered the hopes of his enemies that he would not live long to trouble them. The anxieties and privations of the recent campaign had not failed to aggravate his malady, and, on reaching Brundusium, his enfeebled constitution utterly broke down. He lay for some weeks between life and death, and a report that he had actually succumbed was widely believed. [8]

* * *

So, naturally, Octavian did not behave very healthily or gloriously in the war against Pompey the Great's son Sextus Pompeius.

The curious health pattern repeated itself at the decisive naval engagement of Naulochus against Sextus Pompeius in 36 BC, during which the future Augustus was said to have lain on his back in a stupor, not getting up until Agrippa had fought and defeated the enemy. That was Antony's story, and one can imagine the extrovert Antony . . . indulging in scornful laughter. It must have looked as if the young man was a physical coward.[9]

In any case, Octavian (later Augustus) was frequently ill, notably in Dalmatia in 33 BC (where he was wounded), and then again as we have seen in 25, during the Cantabrian War in Spain—which he had engaged in, it has been suggested, partly to dispel the smear that he was unwarlike and cowardly. However, his fatigues and anxieties in Spain made him ill once again,[10] and shortly after entering on his eleventh consulship in 23 BC he became so much worse that he believed he was dying. 'He fell ill once more', said Dio, 'so as to have no hope of recovery: at any rate he arranged everything as if he was about to die.'[11]

As Firth wrote,

> If the story [of 23 BC] is genuine—and we cannot be certain that it is not either a clever invention of later times to illustrate by a crowning instance the dissimulation of Augustus, or merely one of those canards which purport to relate what takes place in the privacy of palaces—if Augustus really believed that he was on the point of death when he left this cruel enigma to torture and perplex the public mind, no condemnation can be too severe for such cynical irony, though in one sense it needed but this to round off a career of studied hypocrisy. . . .[12]

His physician Antonius Musa, though much disapproved of, saved his life, by a course of cold baths and cold fomentations,[13] and was honoured by a statue bought by public subscription and set up beside a statue of Aesculapius—though he failed to save the life of Marcellus (married to Augustus's only daughter Julia) in the following year.

> Although there is no written authority to warrant the suspicion, it is perhaps permissible to suggest that Augustus deliberately caused the reports as to the gravity of his illness to be exaggerated, and made political capital out of his undoubtedly feeble and precarious health. It was clearly his policy to bring sharply home to his people a sense of their dependence upon him.[14]

And yet, even in this young man's world and in spite of his burden of illnesses, Augustus lived on for another thirty-seven years.[15]

* * *

He dealt with all these manifestations of ill-health very seriously; indeed he took many precautions, of which something has already been said:

> In summer he slept with the bedroom door open, or in the courtyard beside a fountain, having someone to fan him; and could not bear the rays even of the winter sun, but always wore a broad-brimmed hat when he

walked in the open air, even at home. He preferred to
travel by litter, at night, and his bearers kept so
leisurely a pace that they were two days in arriving at
Praeneste [Palestrina] or Tibur [Tivoli]; yet, wherever
it was possible to reach his destination by sea, he did
so. Indeed, he pampered his health, especially by not
bathing too often and being usually content with an
oil-rub—or with a sweat-bath beside a fire, after
which he took a douche of water either warmed or al-
lowed to stand in the sun until it had lost its chill.
When hot brine or warm Albulan water was prescribed for his rheumatism he did no more than sit on
a wooden bath-seat—calling it by the Spanish name
dureta—and alternately dip his hands and feet into the
bath. . . .

[He] took immense care of his health. He sounds at
times like an advanced case of hypochondria. It is true
that in ancient times to catch pneumonia, for example,
meant death. Augustus was all too conscious that this
was so—and could by no stretch of the imagination be
described as taking risks with his bodily health. . . .
He 'never walked in the open air without wearing a
broad-brimmed hat, even at home'. . . . And those
privileged to be the spectators of his daily walks would
be able to see him conclude them with a burst of jog-
ging—after he had wrapped himself round with a
cloak or a blanket.[16]

* * *

The worst affliction of Augustus was his devotion to astrology, that
ancient sign of failure of nerve—the art or pseudo-science of the effect
of heavenly bodies on human destiny, including the belief that earthly
happenings could be forecast because they depended on heaven.

It may seem strange to some that astrology is included as one
of the maladies of the Sick Caesars. And indeed, if anyone finds this
intolerable, let him or her skip the present passage and go on to
what follows. Nevertheless, I do persist in regarding astrology as one
of the troubles of the Sick Caesars. True, millions of other people,
too, believed in it: believed that the sun, moon and stars influenced
the behaviour and actions of the human race. Yet the correct conclusion, in my opinion, is that they all suffered from this particular
weakness, that is to say from this kind of ill-health. True, also, that
innumerable people today believe in astrology. So they, too, suffer
from this kind of mental ill-health. For ill-health, in my view, it is;
it is totally wrong, and if believed in will cause people to take peculiar and often wholly erroneous actions.

Augustus became keen on the fatalistic superstition of astrology at an early age, and was particularly devoted to the astrologer
Theogenes. At Apollonia (Pojani), Augustus and Agrippa together
visited the house of Theogenes the astrologer, and climbed upstairs
to his observatory; they both wished to consult him about their future careers. Agrippa went first and was prophesied such almost in-
credibly good fortune that Augustus expected a far less encouraging
response, and felt ashamed to disclose the time of his birth. Yet

when at last, after a deal of hesitation, he grudgingly supplied the information for which both were pressing him, Theogenes rose and flung himself at his feet; and this gave Augustus so implicit a faith in the destiny awaiting him that he even ventured to publish his horoscope.[17]

Not only was this idea not entirely new, but many later emperors, too, suffered from a similar obsession (almost all of them: Trajan is an exception), which could not fail to amend their behaviour. Augustus's belief in astrology convinced him that the world was ruled entirely by fate.[18] People loved astrological horoscopes because they seemed (quite erroneously) to teach them how to deceive the heavens and dodge destiny (it was not surprising, therefore, that soothsayers were condemned, for that reason: their horoscopes seemed a threat to the lives of the emperors, as the experience of Theogenes foreshadowed).[19] In a sense this was not altogether unprecedented, because the Romans had always believed in divination, upon which astrology, as it were, supervened—it became illegal, but remained irrepressible, and was winked at so long as it kept clear of state affairs. It is still highly frequent today,[20] although absolute nonsense.

Augustus showed his keen interest in astrology, and belief in his star, by often depicting the capricorn on his coinage. The capricorn, as Mattingly and Sydenham remark:

> a fabulous creature, half goat and half fish, appears frequently on the coins of Augustus. The constellation Capicornus, under which Augustus was born, was regarded as a sign of good fortune. Thus on the coins the

capricorn is frequently accompanied by cornucopiae
and rudder, or appears holding a globe with its
forefeet. Sometimes a star is placed above. The type
varies slightly in its meaning according to its attributes. Its reference is primarily to Augustus himself.
Accompanied by the attributes of Fortuna, the capricorn may have a votive significance or may be merely
an expression of the emperor's implicit belief in his
horoscope. When accompanied by a star it perhaps
emphasises the divine nature of Augustus. . . . Libra
[was] the constellation which at this critical moment
was just rising above the Eastern horizon . . . astrologers had been expelled from Rome in BC 33 [by
Agrippa] . . . the capricorn . . . was associated with
eastern mysticism and astrology.[21]

Elsewhere Mattingly deals with the awkward fact that the
capricorn was not, in fact, the astrological sign presiding over Augustus's birth.

The capricorn was the natal sign of Augustus, and was
used by him as a coin-type, as this coin proves and as
Suetonius expressly tells us. . . . Suetonius states that
Augustus was born at day-break, September 23, BC 63.
But Libra, not Capricorn, was the sign then rising at
the eastern point—a serious difficulty. . . . The problem has been solved by J. B. Smyly and A. E. Hous-

man. The moon was in Capricorn at the birth of Augustus. I am indebted to Professor Housman for his help over this point. . . . [At an uncertain Spanish mint] the capricorn is accompanied here by another, which shows, with the capricorn, Aurora hovering in the air—a reference to the hour of Augustus's birth.[22]

CHAPTER III

TIBERIUS

Tiberius, emperor from AD 14 to 37 in succession to Augustus, was born in 42 BC. He was the son of Tiberius Claudius Nero and Livia, who was divorced in order to marry Octavian (the future Augustus) in 38 BC, shortly before the birth of her second son Drusus the elder. During the reign of Augustus, Tiberius had a brilliant military career. After a period of pique at the prominence of Augustus's grandson Gaius Caesar (which had caused Tiberius to retire to Rhodes, 6 BC), Tiberius—after the deaths of Gaius and his brother Lucius—was recognised as his successor (AD 4). He succeeded to the throne ten years later. As emperor, Tiberius remained loyal to the memory and policies of Augustus. Despite the death of his popular nephew and general Germanicus (AD 19), he dealt effectively with a good many legionary and foreign troubles, with the help of Sejanus of Volsinii, praetorian prefect, who became particularly powerful after the death of Tiberius's son Drusus the younger (AD 23). But the reign was disfigured by a heavy incidence of trials for treason *(maiestas)*. Its decisive moment, however, was the emperor's departure in AD 26 for the island of Capreae (Capri), from which he did not return. Sejanus was among those who were subsequently arrested and executed (AD 31).

Tiberius had a paunch, and spindling legs, because of a long illness. He had huge, rather weak eyes (though he saw well in the dark), and hammer-toes. His left hand was more agile than his right. He drank a good deal—as a young man he was nicknamed after drink, Biberius Caldius Mero. 'The gods alone know how he managed to lead his sort of life and still keep physically fit, but he did, perhaps because he fished, rode and swam.'[1] He even feigned illness, so as not to be compelled to say or do anything definite. Arruntius saw him as a good example of someone who was transformed and deranged by absolute power. Like other rulers, he was terrified by the fear of conspiracies—and the delicately balanced system of Augustus was beyond Tiberius and the others.

The decisive moment of Tiberius's reign was his departure for Capreae in AD 26. 'In my sixty-ninth year', Alan Massie imagines him as saying, 'I left Rome. I hope never to see the city again. It has become ugly to me. I could not attend the Senate without experiencing nausea, occasioned by my awareness of that body's degeneracy. A day spent there—no, even a morning—left me oppressed with an intolerable heaviness, a lassitude, the sensation that I had lost all sense of freedom, that I was seized with painful and disabling cramps, even to the point of paralysis.'[2]

Certainly, he got fed up with the senators, who contributed a good deal to his weariness with public business. He lacked, or despised, Augustus's ability to get on with them, though they had to do what he told them. But there were also various other reasons for his departure for Capreae. He acquired a dislike for his chief minister Sejanus (whom he later got rid of). And he had had more than

enough of his mother Livia, and his other female relations such as
Agrippina the elder, the widow of Germanicus. Moreover, Capreae
was relatively safe as regards plots: it only had two landing places.
But I am inclined to think that Alan Massie is right in saying that
his health was also affected: though I believe he is wrong about the
details. What was really Tiberius's trouble was that his face was covered with sores and blotches, so that he had to make use of plaster.
What exactly was the matter with him we do not know—Galen
called it *herpetes*. Tiberius did not stand alone as a sufferer from this
complaint, whatever it was, or from the pimples that accompanied
it; but after all he was the emperor, and it embarrassed him that his
physical appearance became increasingly bizarre. The senators, who
anyway were prepared to criticise him, would have found good reason for carping comment about this, and Tacitus is surely right in
declaring that one of the reasons for Tiberius's withdrawal to
Capreae was his facial disfigurement.³ He liked eating cucumbers,
possibly in order to soothe his skin. Yet he was proud that for many
years he had never called in a doctor, or asked one to send him medicine; he disliked medical men, like Cato the elder, although he followed Augustus in his faith in astrologers, notably Thrasyllus, who
narrowly survived execution and became his friend (issuing an erroneous horoscope).

Thrasyllus inspired the historian Tacitus to make the following comment, in favour of good astrology:

When I hear this [Thrasyllus] and similar stories I feel
uncertain whether human affairs are directed by Fate's

unalterable necessity—or by chance. On this question
the wisest ancient thinkers and their disciples differ . . . they insist that heaven is unconcerned with our
births and deaths. . . . Most men, however, find it natural to believe . . . that the science of prophecy is ver-
ified by remarkable testimonials, ancient and modern,
and that unfulfilled predictions are due merely to ig-
norant impostors who discredit it.[4]

As time went on, however, Tiberius's grip on reality became
weaker, and his notorious dissimulation stronger; he increasingly
feared plots (despite the relative safety of Capreae), and in his last
years he became almost unhinged. He was a humourless, obstinate
old man with a pathological anxiety neurosis and a marked streak
of cruelty in his nature. . . . Not mad, probably, but on the border-
line of madness, misery and loneliness.

Finally, he became really and fatally sick, and it was generally
realised that he was unlikely to recover, although there are several
different accounts of how and why he actually died.[5]

CHAPTER IV

CALIGULA

G AIUS (CALIGULA) BECAME EMPEROR IN SUCCESSION TO TIBERIUS, and ruled from AD 37 to 41. He was the son of Tiberius's nephew Germanicus and his wife Agrippina the elder, daughter of Agrippa and of Julia, the daughter of Augustus. He was born in AD 12 at Antium (Anzio), and after the death of Germanicus (19) lived in Rome with his mother until she was arrested (29), and later (32) joined Tiberius on Capreae. It was generally thought that, as the only surviving son of Germanicus, he must succeed to the principate, but apart from election as *pontifex* and *quaestor* he received no training in public life. Nevertheless, he became emperor in 37, and after a serious illness, executed the praetorian prefect Macro, who had supported his appointment as emperor. He also executed at Moguntiacum (Mainz) Cnaeus Cornelius Lentulus Gaetulicus, who was conspiring against his life. His government was more openly autocratic than that of his predecessors, and he governed with a good deal of cruelty. In many respects he seems to have abandoned the Augustan form of principate in favour of monarchy of the undisguised Greek type. He was murdered in 41.

Was Caligula bad or mad?[1] Opinions have differed. When a

man has, shall we say, deposited the corpses of a number of young women beneath his floor-boards, should he be considered bad or mad? If the former, he should go to a prison, if the latter he should not—a lifetime in Broadmoor may be equally disagreeable, but it is not the same thing. There has been a good deal of modern literature about the madness, or 'neuroses' or otherwise, of leaders.[2]

Tacitus remarks on Gaius's state:

> Gaius was, in fact, sick both physically and mentally. In his boyhood, he suffered from epilepsy; and although in his youth he was not lacking in endurance, there were times when he could hardly walk, stand, think, or hold up his head, owing to sudden faintness. He was well aware that he had mental trouble, and sometimes proposed taking a leave of absence from Rome to clear his brain. Caesonia is reputed to have given him an aphrodisiac which drove him mad. Insomnia was his worst torment. Three hours a night of fitful sleep were all that he ever got, and even then terrifying visions would haunt him. . . . I am convinced that this brain-sickness accounted for his two contradictory vices—overconfidence and extreme timorousness.[3]

It is difficult to say, at a given moment, whether a man is bad or mad. English judges often have this decision to make: should they send someone to prison for life, or should they entrust him to Broadmoor for an indefinite period? Today, this dilemma often occurs: ought a mur-

derer to be imprisoned, or has he been suffering from some mental ailment? With regard to the rulers of the ancient Roman world, we have
the same problem, and it is often scarcely soluble. Moreover, it is exac-
erbated by the enormous power that these men possessed. They were absolute rulers of the entire world from the Atlantic to the Euphrates, as
has already been pointed out, and this meant that they could do what
they more or less pleased. In the case of Caligula this situation was ren-
dered all the more acute because, although quite a young man, he had
spent the last few years in silence and inaction at the gloomy retreat of
the curmudgeonly and elderly Tiberius, so that his natural instincts
were bottled up. All the more understandable it is, therefore, that once
he had become emperor of the vast Roman empire, responsible to no
one, that he began to indulge in bizarre and uncontrollable behaviour.

As Roy Porter wrote,

> There is of course nothing new in focusing attention
> upon the lives of the neurotic and insane. . . . Usually
> the aim has been to plumb the hidden depths of their
> mental illness; sometimes it has been to acquit them
> of madness altogether. . . . Throughout this book I
> have referred to the 'mad' as a generic term for the
> whole range of people thought to be, in some way,
> more or less, abnormal in ideas or behaviour. This
> label is obviously unsatisfactory.[4]

There are examples of clinical madness, legal insanity and
temporary derangement, but for the most part the characters are

studies in over-dedication to an ideal or to a political objective. Some have drastically altered the course of history by their acts, and some have merely changed the flow of the times. Each character has left his peculiar imprint on the history of mankind.[5]

As for Caligula, the ancient writers considered that he was mad. This, for example, is what Suetonius said:

> Gaius paid no attention to traditional or current fashions in dress: ignoring male conventions and even the human decencies. . . . [His] frantic and reckless behaviour roused murderous thoughts in certain minds.[6]

This reference to epilepsy has been taken up in modern times:

> [Gaius] was subject to epileptic fits: epilepsy was in the family. . . . When they occur frequently, they lead to softening of the brain. . . . When the attacks are frequent . . . the afflicted person becomes subject to the wildest caprices and paroxysms of anger without apparent cause. . . . There can be little doubt that the sickness mentioned by the historians, but not, unfortunately, described by them was a violent attack of epileptic fits, which, when they passed, left Gaius in a measure deranged. . . . Whatever his malady was, the prince rose from it very much changed, if not in disposition, at all events in conduct.[7]

A general extravagance of behaviour . . . developed

as he came to feel the power of his position, and as his equilibrium, both physical and psychological, was disturbed. Philo, the acute Jewish observer, remarked, 'heavy drinking and a taste for delicacies, an insatiable appetite even on a swollen stomach, hot baths at the wrong time, emetics followed immediately by further drinking and the gluttony that goes with it, indecent behaviour with boys and women, and all the vices which destroy body and soul and the bonds which unite them, attacked him simultaneously.' No wonder that his judgment became uncertain and his conduct utterly capricious.[8]

It was not unnatural that a Jewish writer should consider Caligula mad, because he was so anti-Jewish (*cf.* below). But Martin Charlesworth appreciated that he was peculiar because, after the stuffy, dangerous household of Tiberius, he had attained uncontrollable autocratic power.

It is not surprising that . . . he should have realised . . . the sweets and possibilities of autocracy, and finally been ruined by its overpowering influence. Herein Josephus is correct in contrasting the earlier and the later Gaius, his mind overbalanced by power. Most of our sources, however, content with the thought that Gaius was 'mad', present a nightmarish disorder of events and actions, in which the character of Gaius has

been so distorted by hatred and sensationalism that we
cannot hope to see clear, and can only deplore the loss
of the more sober Tacitus—although we have still got
certain statements that he made on the subject.[9]

When Caligula fell ill, towards the end of 37, did that affect
his mental equilibrium? Possibly not.

In October [37] came the illness which caused appre-
hensions everywhere, and caused prayers that were certainly sincere to rise for his recovery. . . . We are not
informed about the nature of the illness, and what is
reported about the insomnia from which Gaius suffered and the epilepsy to which he had been subject
since childhood, and what we learn from various
episodes about the delicacy of his health, is not necessarily more closely related to this illness than to the
general disposition of his physique, no doubt tainted
like that of the other young men of the family and
subjected in addition to the strain of unremitting intemperance. The illness was probably a result of this
intemperance. That people should have subsequently
seen in it the immediate cause of a mental derangement is only too easy to explain, granted the apparent
change which they wished to detect in his outward behaviour. But perhaps the difference between the periods before and after the illness should be minimised,

and attributed not so much to a mental disturbance as to the build-up of a sort of exasperation with his sense of unlimited authority in a weak man devoid of moral principles and ill-prepared for the responsible use of the immense power with which he had been invested more by chance than through any real merits. . . . [We may doubt] the validity of a simplistic contrast between early days of unalloyed happiness and a sequel of gloomy tyranny, ushered in by the affliction of an unexpected bout of madness. Probably the illness brought nothing more than the confirmation of a young man intoxicated with power in a dream of complete absolutism.[10]

The situation was intensified, or perhaps obscured, by the Jewish writers, who had to report on Caligula's intense hostility to the Jews, on the grounds (foreshadowing the First Jewish Revolt) that they alone rejected the religious and social basis on which the Roman empire was constituted.[11] Some of them were convinced that his illness of 37 had turned his mind, others considered that 39 was the decisive moment. For example,

Philo . . . believes that the serious illness which Gaius suffered at the end of AD 37 left its mark upon his character, and that, although he recovered from it, he was afterwards a moral wreck and a cruel tyrant. The silence of all our other authorities prevents us from ac-

cepting this most convenient theory. . . . No other
writer gives Philo his support. Josephus declares that
Gaius ruled well for two years, dating the change in
his character to AD 38 or 39. . . . That Gaius changed
the character of his government, chiefly his attitude to
the Senate, in AD 39 is certain.[12]

Let us conclude, then, that Caligula was seriously ill in 37,
but that his government definitely became more cruel and autocratic in 39. 'The precise nature of the malady from which he suffered', wrote Charlesworth, 'may never be determined; all our
sources agree in recording the frenzied energy that hurried him on,
and Suetonius has a pitiful picture of sleepless nights, when he
would wander restlessly through the Palace crying for the dawn; in
any case it is a matter more for the psychiatrist than the historian.'

But the historian, nevertheless, has to go back to the question: what was wrong with Caligula? Hyperthyroidism, acute encephalitis or simply some unknown serious illness have all been
suggested.

A. A. Barrett wrote in these terms:

In Suetonius Caligula is depicted as a stark lunatic of
the megalomaniac type, in the account of an eyewit-
ness, Philo, he appears as a fidgety neurotic. Though
his behaviour perhaps fell short of madness, it is impossible to determine the degree of rationality he re-
tained, especially in view of the nature of the sources.

Did he, for instance, intend to make his favourite horse Incitatus consul, or is the rumour baseless? Balsdon tried to find some reason behind his military movements. When, wearing the breastplate of Alexander the Great, he drove over a bridge of boats which he had built across the Bay of Naples, was he showing mere eccentricity or megalomania?

Because of the distortions in the historical tradition, it is very difficult to determine to what degree Caligula might be considered mentally and physically fit for the task of being emperor. It does appear that in his early years he suffered from delicate health. He was prone to epileptic fits, and Augustus was concerned enough in AD 14 to appoint two doctors to accompany him when he travelled north to join his parents. As he grew older, his strength gradually improved, but fainting fits still at times made it difficult for him to walk or stay standing up. There are signs that he continued to be troubled by various ailments as an adult, such as his serious illness in 38, and his stomach-ache on the day of his death. . . . It is clear that Caligula was highly strong and nervous. . . . It comes as no surprise that he suffered from insomnia (to which Augustus also was prone). . . . Even when he did manage to fall into sleep, it was fitful and disturbed by vivid nightmares.[13]

I myself ventured to sum up the controversy as follows:

[Gaius] has been variously labelled epileptic, schizoid, schizophrenic or just chronically alcoholic. Tacitus described his mind as disordered and upset, but Caligula was probably not mad in any accepted sense of the term; though diagnoses by modern psychologists or physicians are useless, because there is not adequate evidence to go on. . . . He used to get very excited. Anger provoked him to violent outpourings of words, and he would fidget about nervously while continuing to shout at the top of his voice. He was a young man of frantic energy, but his powers of application failed to last. He could start all manner of things, but found it almost impossible to finish them. Caligula's sharp tongue continually caused dismay. Very often this was precisely his intention.[14]

Probably Balsdon's is the best conclusion:

Our authorities do not enlighten us concerning the character of his illness [AD 37]. Today it would probably be described as a nervous breakdown; that seems to have been Philo's impression. He declares that the constitution of Gaius was not able to support the sudden change from the austerity of private life (on Capreae, be it observed) to the eating and drinking and loving, the emetics and the hot baths, in which he now indulged. . . . Philo, Josephus, and Cassius Dio, in one way or another, speak of his 'mania', though Josephus believed that this mania was able at times to be discarded. Seneca asserts that the pallor of his face was evidence of *'insania'*, and Tacitus speaks of him as being 'impetuously minded'—*'commotus ingenio'*—and refers to his *'turbata mens'*. . . . He certainly suffered, like Julius Caesar, from epileptic fits. . . . But in this event the 'madness' cannot have developed until late in AD 39. . . . It was the belief of many of his contemporaries and the conviction of succeeding generations that Gaius was mentally retarded. . . . [But] nowhere is the theory propounded or developed that he was simply a madman. . . . The great popularity which he won in the city of Rome in the first few months of his government, following the general approval of his succession, cannot be explained unless he was then a perfectly normal and attractive young man.[15]

CHAPTER V

CLAUDIUS

CLAUDIUS (TIBERIUS CLAUDIUS NERO GERMANICUS) SUCCEEDED Gaius (Caligula) as emperor in 41, and ruled until AD 54. He was the youngest son of Drusus the elder and Antonia the younger. He was born at Lugdunum (Lyon) in 10 BC. He received no public distinction from Augustus besides the augurate, and held no office under Tiberius. At the beginning of the reign of Gaius (37), however, he became consul with the new emperor, who was otherwise, however, rude to him. After the assassination of Gaius the Praetorian Guard acclaimed him as emperor although the Senate was still arguing about whether to restore the Republic. As emperor, Claudius took part in the invasion of Britain (43) and was actively liberal, but came increasingly under the thumbs of his wives and freedmen. His wife Messalina succumbed in 48 to Narcissus, but then he married his niece Agrippina the younger, who had the backing of Pallas and persuaded Claudius in 50 to adopt her son Nero as guardian of his own son Britannicus. In 54 Claudius died, probably killed by Agrippina, and Nero succeeded him. Claudius was consecrated as a god, the first emperor after Augustus to receive this honour.

There was something unmistakably wrong with Claudius.[1] Suetonius notes:

Though tall, well-built, with a handsome face, a fine
head of white hair and a firm neck, he stumbled as he
walked owing to the weakness of his knees; and . . .
both in his lighter moments and at serious business,
he had several disagreeable traits. These included an
uncontrolled laugh, a horrible habit, under the stress
of anger, of slobbering at the mouth and running at
the nose, a stammer and a persistent nervous tic of the
head, which was apparent at all times but especially
when he exerted himself to the slightest extent. His
health was wretched until he succeeded to the throne,
when it suddenly became excellent, except for violent
stomach-aches which often, he said, made him think
of suicide. . . . It was seldom that Claudius left a din-
ing hall except gorged and sodden. . . . He slept in
short snatches, being usually awake before midnight;
but he would sometimes nod off during the daytime in
Court, and then the lawyers had difficulty in rousing
him, however loud they shouted. . . . Often . . .
Claudius showed such absent-mindedness in speech
and action that it might have been thought that he
neither knew nor cared to whom, or in whose hearing,
or when or where, he was speaking.[2]

The elder Pliny added the curious detail that the new emperor's (Claudius's) eyes had a fleshy cover, streaked with tiny veins,
which at times filled with tears.[3]

What was the matter with him?[4] At this distance of time, with our fragmentary information, we cannot tell. His ailment has been variously diagnosed; and the suggestions have included meningitis, poliomyelitis, pre-natal encephalitis, multiple sclerosis, alcoholism and congenital cerebral paralysis. Evidently the trouble was paralysis of some sort or other, and when he was young it caused him to suffer from a wide variety of obstinate disorders. But in his later years he summoned up the power to overcome his infirmities, so that through his entire reign his health, surprisingly enough, was excellent—with the single exception of recurrent attacks of stomach-ache or heartburn, which were so fierce, he complained, that they almost drove him to suicide.[5]

The confused data handed down from antiquity and the limitations of the psycho-medical sciences make it difficult to draw a picture of Claudius at once satisfactory to the historian, the physician and the psychologist. A conservative reconstruction of the sources suggests that the boy was afflicted with some ailment which, although it did not prevent normal physical growth, kept him in constant ill health and incapacitated him for the activities of his station. . . . Because his bodily ills did not respond quickly to medical treatment, and his intellect did not develop as rapidly as is the wont of normal children, his elders came to fear that he would remain an invalid and a dullard for life. . . . On the threshold of manhood [however],

Claudius's gradual improvement was giving hopes of a complete recovery. . . . [But] every unorthodox word of his, every awkward gesture which ordinarily might have escaped attention was now looked upon as fresh evidence that he was incurable.[6]

Suetonius remarks on Claudius's mental health:

It would seem, however, quite unlikely that Claudius was, or was looked upon, as the idiot which he has sometimes been made out to be. . . . [But] he was far from normal. . . . [However] the diagnosis of insanity of a pronounced type . . . is open to objection on several grounds. . . . I believe that he suffered from one of the forms of infantile spastic paralysis, or infantile diplegia . . . paraplegic rigidity, or Little's Disease. . . . To be sure, in his characteristics and conduct there is evidence of a certain mental or nervous condition which led him at times to acts and processes of thought not consonant with normality.[7]

Indeed, Claudius seemed so abnormal that Augustus was shocked by his condition, and wrote to his wife Livia as follows:

My dear Livia,

As you suggested, I have now discussed with Tiberius what we should do about your grandson

Claudius at the coming Games of Mars. We both agreed that a decision ought to be taken once and for all. The question is whether he has—shall I say?—full command of all his senses. If so, I can see nothing against sending him through the same degrees of office as his brother. But should he be deemed physically and mentally deficient, the public (which always likes to scoff and mock at such things) must not be given a chance of laughing at him and us. I fear that we shall find ourselves in constant trouble if the question of his fitness to officiate in this or that capacity keeps cropping up. We should therefore decide in advance whether he can or cannot be trusted with offices of state. . . .

In short, my dear Livia, I am anxious that a decision should be reached on this matter once and for all, to save us from further alternations of hope and despair. You are at liberty to show this part of my letter to our kinswoman Antonia for her perusal. When you are away, I shall certainly invite young Tiberius Claudius to dine every day, rather than leave him to the exclusive company of Athenodorus and Sulpicius. If only he would show greater concentration and behave with less capriciousness in his choice of someone to imitate in his movements, deportment and gait. I am sorry for the poor fellow, because in serious matters, when not wool-gathering, he shows a very decent character.[8]

Yet Augustus, in spite of his natural affection for the boys in his family, could not overcome the horror he felt for people who were deformed (including dwarfs), whom he regarded as freaks of nature and therefore bringers of bad luck. And Claudius's own mother, Antonia, described him as a monster.[9] Other contemporary sources, too, are altogether against him.

But these sources (which record Tiberius, too, as rejecting Claudius as mentally unfit) are too unkind; and Augustus himself (perhaps reluctantly) admitted his good points to his wife. 'My dear Livia' (he wrote) 'I'll be damned if your grandson Tiberius Claudius hasn't given me a very pleasant surprise! How on earth anyone who talks so confusedly can nevertheless speak in public with such clearness, saying all that needs to be said, I simply do not understand.'[10]

And, indeed, the reign of Claudius was not at all what, reading the ancient historians, one would have expected. The reason for this was directly connected with his earlier and congenital ill-health. Because, having been virtually excluded from public life by Augustus and his successors, Claudius became assiduously devoted to other, cultivated people, spent time, for example, with Greek scholars (when not lonely), was interested in history and phonetics, and his years of study gave him a feeling for Roman tradition and destiny: his education was by no means neglected, and he thought and wrote long and deeply about the past, including the past of Rome. And what a pity that his works have not survived! What a pity, for instance, that we no longer have his *History of the Etruscans*!—about whom we know all too little, because the Romans who should have recorded their story were their conquerors, and therefore notoriously

incomplete in looking back upon them. But we know enough about
this book, and about Claudius's others, to see that he is a classic case
of a person whose ill-health was responsible not only for his temporary retirement but also for the careful thought about past and future history which that retirement was able to bring. True, he was
not without his failings, as one can imagine.[11] Stomach troubles and
drink and sex were among them.[12] He was also extremely timid and
easily terrified, if not cowardly, and was surrounded by bodyguards
(which, indeed, he needed, since his constant fear of conspiracies was
not unjustified). He felt that no one was able to understand him; and
his nerves became worse. But he wanted to overcome his infirmities;[13] and he deserves the praise which his reign earned him.

* * *

Claudius's successor Nero (54-68), despite his irregular life, does not
really come into this book because, throughout his not inconsider-
able reign, he only had three illnesses, none of them serious (and he
did not give up drinking wine). Like so many other Caesars, he became more bloodthirsty when he realised he was threatened by plots.

Nero's successor Galba (68-69), we are told, was of average
height, very bald, with blue eyes and a hooked nose. His hands and
feet were so distorted by gout (*articulari morbo*) that he could not endure a shoe for long, unroll a book or even hold one. The flesh on his
right side, too, had grown out and hung down to such an extent that
it could with difficulty be held in place by a bandage. It is said that
he was a heavy eater.[14]

For 'bandage' read 'truss'. He was badly ruptured, and needed one. Whether he really suffered from gout, or from arthritis as some have suggested, remains uncertain. He died at the age of about seventy-three, an old age for a Roman. Indeed it was said that, having been only a year short of this at the time of his accession, he was surely too old to have been a successful emperor.

Galba's successor Otho (69) was bow-legged, splay-footed, wholly depilated and wore a toupee.[15] The main trouble with the man who briefly followed him, Vitellius (69), was that he ate and drank too much.[16] The successful contestant in the Civil Wars, Vespasian—when he suffered from a slight fever—made himself worse by bathing in cold water and getting a chill on his stomach, which produced diarrhoea and killed him.

CHAPTER VI

DOMITIAN *and* AFTER

V ESPASIAN'S SECOND SON, WHO SUCCEEDED HIS BROTHER TITUS,[1] was Domitian (Titus Flavius Domitianus), emperor 81-96. Born in 51, he had a short experience of power when he was acclaimed as Caesar on Vitellius's death (69). Up to the rebellion of Lucius Antonius Saturninus in 88 he ruled moderately. Thereafter his rule was severe, culminating in a Terror to eliminate plotting (93-96). He enlarged existing absolutist tendencies, including much flattery of himself. In dealing with foreign affairs, he sought to complete the line of northern defence. His government of the empire was efficient and careful. He was very severe on questions affecting public morals. But finally his own wife Domitia felt insecure, and joined with the two praetorian prefects in a conspiracy against his life. It was successful, and Domitian was assassinated in 96. The army was not pleased.

Domitian was a very complicated character, who suffered from certain physical disadvantages. He was tall of stature, with a modest expression and a high colour. His eyes were large, but his sight was somewhat dim. He was handsome and graceful, too, especially when a young man, with the exception of his feet, the toes of which were somewhat cramped. In later life he had the further dis-figurements of baldness, a protruding belly and spindle legs, though the latter had become thin from a long illness.[2]

He was also, at quite an early age, going bald, and was sen-sitive about it. Domitian wrote a book *On Care of the Hair*, but his knowledge of the subject did not do much to remedy his own lack of it. Moreover, he was so sensitive about this condition that if he heard anyone else being mocked for being bald he took it as a per-sonal affront.[3] Or so we are told, but since Martial, who flattered him abysmally, nevertheless made a good deal of fun of men who are bald, Domitian can scarcely have been so touchy on the subject as all that.

However, Domitian was certainly touchy on other subjects, notably his own safety.[4] Like all the Caesars, he feared that there might be a plot against him; and with exceptionally good reason, since he was inhumanly brutal. With a view to this danger, of which he was perpetually afraid, he had all the marble walls in his rooms in the palace highly polished, so that he would see if anyone crept up behind him. He also had bad nerves; when he went on Lake Al-banus (near his country palace) he became nervously upset by the noise the oarsmen made, so that he himself went in a boat towed be-hind. His own personal vice—apart from excessive womanising—was to cut the wings off captured flies.

> At the beginning of his reign he used to spend hours
> in seclusion every day, doing nothing but catch flies
> and stab them with a keenly sharpened stylus. Conse-

quently when someone once asked whether anyone was
in there with Caesar, Vibius Crispus made the witty
reply: 'Not even a fly.'[5]

This was not a very nice habit. Indeed it was the sign of a cold
and cruel man. It is therefore hardly surprising that Domitian, to an
alarming extent, shared the common belief in astrology, with special
concern for his own horoscope.

What disturbed him most . . . was a prediction by the
astrologer Ascletario, and its sequel. This man, when
charged, made no secret of having revealed the future,
which he had foreseen by his magical arts. Domitian at
once asked whether he could prophesy the manner of
his own end, and upon Ascletario replying that he
would very soon be torn to pieces by dogs, had him executed on the spot, and gave orders for his funeral rites
to be conducted with the greatest care, as a further
proof that astrology was a fake.[6]

Or rather, the reason why Domitian paid so much attention
to Ascletario's funeral was *ad coarguendam temeritatem artis*—to prevent the fulfilment of the prophecy. But, in fact—although he
hardly needed an astrologer to warn him of his danger—the emperor
was assassinated shortly afterwards.

* * *

Nerva (Marcus Cocceius), born in *c.* AD 30, was emperor from 96 to
98, in succession to Domitian, whom the Senate had detested. He
was the grandson of the Marcus Cocceius Nerva who was a close
friend of Tiberius. Nerva became consul in 71 with the emperor
Vespasian. When he himself became emperor, he endeavoured to be
progressive and enlightened, spending a lot of money to improve the
administration of Italy and abolishing treason charges (although the
praetorians insisted on the execution of Domitian's assassins). But in
order to keep the army from rebelling he (in the absence of a son of
his own) adopted Trajan, who became consul with him in 98 and
was his obvious heir, though absent in the north.

Nerva was already about sixty-six when he came to the throne.

> Nor was his [Nerva's] age, to senators at least, unwel-
> come. History had enforced the lesson that, however well
> disposed a *princeps* were on his accession, few men could
> withstand the temptations of unlimited power for long;
> an old emperor might die before he became dangerous.[7]

Nerva's health was not very good.[8] He had always vomited up
his food (vomiting defeated Napoleon on his return from Elba). He
died of a feverish chill in 98, at the age of about sixty-eight.

Trajan and Hadrian died at the ages of sixty-four and sixty-
two. It does not seem certain whether they ought to be included in
the present survey, since, although Trajan drank fairly heavily, their
health had remained good until their final illnesses, which were not
unduly early by Roman standards.

Trajan, Roman emperor AD 98-117, was son of Marcus
Ulpius Trajanus and a Spanish mother. Born at Italica in Baetica
(southern Spain) in 53 (or possibly, though less probably, 56), he engaged in military service and was subsequently *quaestor* and *praetor*.
While commanding a legion in Spain he had to deal with the rebellion of Saturninus in Upper Germany (*c.* 88). He was one of the
greatest emperors, personally initiating many reforms in the administration and annexing Dacia as a province. His eastern conquests,
however, were more precarious. But he rehabilitated the mystical
aura of the principate initiated by Augustus.

He died at Selinus (Selindi) in Cilicia, and was suspicious
about what had struck him down.

Dio Cassius writes,

> Trajan himself suspected that his sickness was due to
> poison that had been administered to him; but some
> state that it was because the blood, which descends
> every year into the lower parts of the body, was in his
> case checked in its flow. He had also suffered a stroke,
> so that a portion of his body was paralysed, and he was
> dropsical all over. On coming to Selinus in Cilicia,
> which we also call Trajanopolis, he suddenly expired.[9]

* * *

His successor Hadrian, who was emperor from 117 to 138, was born
in 76, probably at Italica (Santiponce) in Baetica. He was the son of

two persons from Gades (Cadiz); his paternal grandfather had been
married to Trajan's aunt. When his father died in 85, he joined the
household of Trajan, who made him tribune of three successive legions and took him in 100 to Rome, where he married Vibia Sabina.
Thereafter he held various important posts, and was in high favour
with Trajan and his wife Plotina, being designated consul, for the
second time, in 117 for 118. His succession, however, was dubious
and disputed, and Hadrian was not favourably regarded by the
whole of the Senate. Hadrian toured the provinces exceptionally
widely; his boy-friend Antinous died in Egypt in 130. Hadrian also
erected important, innovative buildings in Rome. Weakening in
health, he adopted Aelius Caesar in 136; and after Aelius's death in
138 he turned to Antoninus Pius. Hadrian himself died at Baiae
(Baia) in 138.

He himself had always enjoyed good health, but his final illness caused him misery. According to Dio, he became consumptive
as a result of a great loss of blood (a flow of blood from the nostrils,
to which he had always been subject, became more copious), and this
made him consumptive and subsequently dropsical;[10] although ancient references to tuberculosis and dropsy (cf. Trajan above) always
raise questions.

> Hadrian now began to be sick; for he had been subject
> even before this to a flow of blood from the nostrils,
> and at this time it became distinctly more copious. He
> therefore despaired of his life. . . . Hadrian did linger
> on a long time in his illness, and often desired to kill

himself. . . . He became consumptive as a result of his great loss of life, and this led to dropsy. . . . By certain charms and magic rites Hadrian would be relieved for a time of his dropsy, but would soon be filled with water again. Since, therefore, he was constantly getting worse and might be said to be dying day by day, he began to long for death; often he would ask for poison or a sword, but no one would give them to him. . . . The emperor lamented bitterly the plight to which his malady and his helplessness had brought him, in that he was not able to make away with himself, though he still had the power, even when so near death, to destroy anybody else. Finally he abandoned his careful regimen, and by indulging in unsuitable foods and drinks met his death, shouting aloud the popular saying: 'Many physicians have slain a king.' He had lived sixty-two years, five months and nineteen days.[11] Hadrian had now endured his wasting illness with a gallant patience for many months. It is a fact not without its pathos that he alone of all the Roman emperors issued coins on which was stamped the allegorical figure of PATIENTIA. In the spring of AD 138 the disease took a graver turn. Dropsical supervened over phthisical symptoms, and the unceasing pain became almost unendurable. Not a physician could give him any relief. A late Church Father, a quarrelsome bigot, Epiphanius, speaks of a letter composed and published by Hadrian which derided all medical science.

If this be true, it is no great wonder. Pain is prompter of much bitterness at the powerlessness of human aid. Leaving the administration of Rome and of the empire to Antoninus, the emperor withdrew to Baiae on the warm sunny Bay of Naples. Here quacks and sooth-sayers dogged his steps, dreams and visions of the night disquieted his feverish sleep. Chronicler and bi-ographer dwell at great length and with sorry gusto upon Hadrian's sufferings. . . . For some months he en-dured 'and, as it were, died daily'. . . . So at the last Hadrian's own brave spirit yielded.[12]

But PATIENTIA had not been his strongest point, as these ex-cerpts show. Dio asserted that he became fed up with life, and his at-tack on 'many physicians' suggests that he took the view that he might have regained his health and lived longer if only he had re-ceived proper treatment.[13]

* * *

Antoninus Pius, his successor, had been born in 80 at Lanu-vium, near Rome. He was a very good emperor, whose policy was unsensational, harmonious, beneficent and mildly progressive. He had headaches, but rarely saw a doctor. 'Since he was tall and an old man and stooped', says the *Historia Augusta*, 'he used to be strapped up with lindenwood boards placed on his chest, so that he could walk in an upright posture.'[14] And he ate dried bread. He died in 161, at the age of about seventy-five.

CHAPTER VII

MARCUS AURELIUS
and COMMODUS

THE SUCCESSOR OF ANTONINUS PIUS WAS MARCUS AURELIUS. Marcus Aurelius (Marcus Annius Verus), emperor 161-180, was of a consular family from Spain: his father was Annius Verus, brother of Faustina the elder, wife of Antoninus Pius, whom Marcus Aurelius succeeded on the throne. Marcus Aurelius's mother was Domitia Lucilla, whose family possessed a large tile factory near Rome, which Marcus inherited. Hadrian (emperor 117-138) nicknamed him *Verissimus*, made him a Salian priest when he was only eight, arranged for his engagement in 136 to the daughter of Lucius Aelius (heir to the throne until his death in 137), and saw to his elaborate education. On Hadrian's death, Antoninus Pius, now emperor, adopted him—along with Lucius Verus, the son of Lucius Aelius—and after holding the consulship with Antoninus (140) he became engaged to the latter's daughter, the younger Faustina, in 145. When Marcus became emperor, he arranged that Lucius Verus should become his colleague and the fiancé of Marcus's daughter Lucilla. Lucius Verus left for the east, where his generals won victories against the Parthians, but the Roman army brought back the plague

to the west. In *c.* 166 German tribes crossed the upper and lower
Danube and invaded north Italy. Marcus made Dacia a consular
province, and in 168 he and Verus were at Aquileia, and the Germans sought terms. Marcus envisaged the annexation of central and
south-eastern Europe north of the Danube, and, after the death of
Verus (169) fought successfully against the Germans, but his plans
were shelved after the rebellion of Avidius Cassius in the east. Avidius was assassinated and Marcus moved to the east, but following a
new German threat (177) Marcus promoted his son Commodus to
become his colleague, and left him in Rome while he moved to carry
out his German designs.

Marcus Aurelius presented a considerable health problem. As
he wrote himself:

> He was so frail of body that at first he could not en-
> dure the cold. But even after the soldiers had assem-
> bled at his command he would retire before addressing
> a word to them. And he took but very little food and
> that always at night. It was never his practice to eat
> during the daytime, unless it were some of the drug
> called theriac. This drug he took, not so much because
> he feared anything, as because his stomach and chest
> were in bad condition. And it is reported that this
> practice enable him to endure both this and other mal-
> adies. . . . He could not display many feats of physical
> prowess. Yet he had developed his body from a very
> weak one to one capable of the greatest endurance. . . .

As a result of his close application and study he was
extremely frail in body, though in the beginning he
had been so vigorous that he used to fight in armour,
and would strike down wild boars while on horse-
back. . . . He was not strong in body.[1]

We also have the great advantage that the eminent doctor
Galen not only visited him when he was sick but wrote about the
experience—and his writing has survived.

What happened in the case of the emperor himself was
really wonderful. His own opinion and that of the
physicians of his entourage who had gone abroad with
him was that some febrile paroxysm had begun. But
they all proved wrong both on the second and third
day, in the morning and at the third hour. He had on
the preceding day taken a draught of bitter aloes at the
first hour, and then some theriac as was his daily custom. Next he took some food about the sixth hour,
washed at sunset, and had a small meal. During the
whole night there ensued colicky pains with intestinal
evacuations. This made him feverish, and when his at-
tendant physicians observed this, they gave orders that
he should be kept quiet; then they prescribed slop diet
at the ninth hour. After this I was myself also summoned to come and sleep in the palace. Then, when
the lamps were newly lit, a messenger came to call me

at the emperor's bidding. Three doctors had been ob-
serving him since about daybreak, and two of them feeling his pulse, and they all considered this the beginning
of a febrile attack. I stood by, however, without saying
anything; so the emperor, looking at me first, asked why,
when the others felt his pulse, I alone did not do so. I
said to him, 'Two of the gentlemen have already done
this, and probably when they were abroad with you they
already learned by experience the characteristics of your
pulse, hence I expect they will be better able to judge its
present condition (*diathesis*).' On my saying this he bade
me also feel his pulse. It seemed to me that, taking his
age and constitution into account, the pulse was far from
indicating the beginning of a febrile attack. I declared
that this was no onset of fever, but that his stomach was
overloaded by the food he had taken, which had turned
to phlegm, prior to ejection. My diagnosis seemed
praiseworthy to the emperor, and he repeated three times
in succession: 'That's it. It is just what you say. I feel I
have taken too much cold food.' And he asked what was
to be done I answered what I knew, and said to him, 'If
it were anyone else who was in this state, I should follow
my custom and give him wine sprinkled with pepper.
But in the case of kings like yourself, physicians are in
the habit of giving safer remedies; hence it will be
enough to apply over your stomach some wool impreg-
nated with warm spikenard ointment.'

The emperor said that in any case when his stomach
was out of order he was in the habit of applying warm
spikenard ointment enveloped in purple wool. So he
gave orders to Pitholaus to do this, and to let me go.
When this application had been made, and his feet
thoroughly heated by rubbing with the warm hand, he
asked for some Sabine wine, sprinkled pepper on it,
and drank.[2]

This is what Marcus Aurelius himself said about health:

In the case of every pain, be ready with the thought
that it is not dishonourable and doesn't harm the mind
that holds the helm. . . . This saying of Epicurus
should help you—'pain is neither unbearable nor un-
ending, so long as you remember its limitations and
don't add to it with your imagination.' . . . 'On pain:
what we cannot bear takes us away [from life]; what
lasts can be borne.' 'Pain in the hand and foot is not
against nature, provided that the foot and hand are
fulfilling their own tasks. Hence not even for a man is
pain contrary to nature. If it's not contrary to nature,
it's not evil for him.'[3]

Apollonius . . . schooled me to meet spasms of
acute pain . . . and the tedium of a chronic ailment
with the same unaltered composure. . . . I must thank
heaven . . . for remedies prescribed me in dreams—

especially in cases of blood-spitting and vertigo, as happened Caieta [Gaeta] and Chrysa.[4]

As I wrote in *The Antonines:*

What was the matter with [Marcus Aurelius]? Did he suffer from pulmonary tuberculosis? Or a gastric ulcer? Or migraine? Or some more obscure complaint of the blood? And at what stages of his life did these troubles become better, or, more probably, worse? These are things that we shall never know. But we do know that he had a pain in his chest as a youth, that in later life troubles occurred, and that the physician Galen gave him, every day, a drug from the imperial stores named *theriac*. This, normally, consisted of one part seed-clover, one of a species of the herb birthwort, one of wild rue and one of pounded pulse, and was taken in pills with wine. The drug had been prescribed for Mithridates VI of Pontus and Nero ('viper's flesh') as an antidote to possible poisoning. But it was also prescribed for various illnesses, and Aurelius probably took it as a pain-killer and sleeping draught, since he found it difficult to sleep, and theriac made him drowsy. Galen probably put mandragora in it, or perhaps opium.[5]

Marcus Aurelius's death, in 180, has been the subject of much discussion.[6] It is not certain what he died of. We can disregard

the rumour, reported by Dio, that Commodus (his son) was responsible. But Aurelius was not very strong.

In his biography of Marcus Aurelius, Birley writes,

> He was so weak physically that at first he could not en-
> dure the cold and, even after the soldiers had assembled
> at his command, would withdraw without addressing a
> word to them. He ate very little food, and that always at
> night.
>
> He could not take anything in the daytime, ex-
> cept some of the medicine called *theriac*. This he
> took not so much because he was afraid of anything,
> but because he was suffering from a chest and stom-
> ach condition. . . . The medicine which Marcus took
> was prescribed for him by Galen. It contained
> opium. Galen records that Marcus stopped taking it
> because it made him drowsy, but then found he
> could not sleep, and had to take a regular dose
> again.
>
> This *may* indicate that he had become an opium
> addict. But Marcus did not become a helpless addict
> like Thomas de Quincey. And the attempt to dis-
> cover traces of the opium eater's confused and dis-
> torted imagination in the *Meditations* has not been
> very convincing. It is reasonable to suppose that he
> took the opium as a pain-killer and as a sleeping-
> draught.[7]

In fact, Marcus Aurelius probably did not become an opium addict at all, or die of any such addiction, and attempts to demonstrate that he did have proved unsuccessful.

The emperor was in the habit, said T. W. Africa,[8] of taking a certain small quantity of theriac. When he discovered that he was getting somnolent, he had the poppy-juice removed from the compound. When sleepless nights ensued, he was compelled to return to the preparation containing the juice. Marcus Aurelius took theriac as a general medicine, not exclusively in order to survive possible poisoning. This is what historical novelist Amanda Prantera thought happened:

> We both of us [Galen and the historian Dio Cassius] knew without a doubt that Marcus in his midnight raid on the camp medical chest had been after poppy-juice: soothing and sleep-inducing extracts which normally formed a staple ingredient of his evening theriac, but which recently had been deliberately removed from the brew on my instructions precisely because it was so soothing and sleep-inducing. This was the course we had always adopted in the past. . . . The extract had been suspended. With, I may add, as in the past, Marcus's full consent.[9]

This was based on what Galen himself wrote. Galen is not always reliable—in particular, he exaggerated the success of his treatments, and his closeness to the emperor—but what he says on this subject is worth reading, and probably trustworthy.

About Antoninus [Marcus Aurelius] I know personally
that for his own safety he used to prepare and take [the
medicine] each day . . . swallowing this either with or
without admixture of water or wine or the like. And
when he began to get very drowsy at his daily occupa-
tions, he took away the poppy-juice [from the mixture:
as we saw]. Then, owing to his former custom . . . he
began again to pass the greater part of the night without sleep. Hence he was forced once more to take some
of the mixture which contained poppy-juice, as this
had now become more or less habitual with him. (I
have often said already that such drugs had a milder action on him when they were taken for a length of time.)

The emperor was then, on account of the German
war, in the Danube region, and I had been excused
from serving in the campaign. He used to speak
highly of the antidote of Demetrius, his principal
physician (*archiatrus*), and, after the latter's death, he
wrote to Euphrates, his general agent (or Intendant
General: *catholicus*), from whom he used to get the
simples for compounding, asking him to say who was
with him of those who drew an imperial salary. On
learning that I had always been with him when the
compositions were made, he gave orders that the antidote should be prepared by me. This was the only one
that pleased him; so on coming to Rome he enquired
in what proportion I used the simple drugs in my

preparation. . . . Antoninus [Aurelius] took the medicine every day with plenty of honey.[10]

Marcus Aurelius died in AD 180. But we still do not know for
certain why Marcus Aurelius died. A. J. Brock, as we have seen, suggested that he may have had some kind of ulcer, and that is possible
and probably a cause of his death; but not certain. Anyway, he does
not seem to have died because of addiction to opium, given him by
Galen. Nor is the theory that he suffered from small-pox, as a result
of the plague, very plausible.

Indeed, it is by no means certain that what we call small-pox
existed in ancient times. Many of the older school of medical historians held that small-pox was known in Greece and Rome, some
being of the opinion that the plague of Athens (430 BC) and the
plague of Galen (AD 164–180) were small-pox. But this view is not
generally accepted. In 1901 Paul Kübler made the pertinent obser-
vation that there is no known classical statue or caricature which
portrays a pock-marked face and no mention of any such disfigure-
ment by medical or lay authors. The typical pock-mark could hardly
have escaped notice.[11]

Aurelius is also said to have died from the plague, hard
though that too is to identify.[12] It is possibly, in any case, that it
was his ill-health which prevented him from invading Germany
from the south and annexing it. His son Commodus was against
the idea, as we shall see. And the revolt of Avidius Cassius (175)
has been blamed for the cancellation of Aurelius's plan to invade
Germany. That may well be true, but it also remains probable that

if Aurelius had been feeling better he would have persevered with the invasion.

* * *

Marcus Aurelius was succeeded by his very temperamental son Commodus, who immediately (perhaps under the influence of his Greek adviser Saoterus) gave up the plan to invade Germany and returned to Rome.

Commodus had gradually advanced to the position of joint-ruler, which he attained in 177. After his accession in 180, peace on the German frontiers comprised the imposition of restrictions and controls upon the tribes in return for subsidies and the evacuation of occupied territory—a justifiable policy. Commodus maintained peace on all frontiers—the only serious trouble was in Britain, where the Antonine Wall was overrun, the situation being restored by Ulpius Marcellus. Commodus loved the role of gladiator at Rome. He became much nastier, especially to the Senate, after an abortive conspiracy directed by Lucilla (the widow of Lucius Verus) and Ummidius Quadratus (182). For the next ten years Rome was virtually governed by the praetorian prefects Perennis (182-85) and Cleander (186-89), and thereafter by Commodus's mistress Marcia, his chamberlain Eclectus and Laetus, who became praetorian prefect in 192.

As I wrote in *The Antonines:*

As for Commodus himself, it is likely that he was not really fit to be emperor.[13] His appearance, it is true,

was impressive, although he suffered from what seems
to have been an unsightly hernia of the groin. Commodus had something wrong with him in the groin,
which stuck out so much that the Roman people could
detect the swelling through his silk clothing. Many
verses were written on this subject, and Marius Maximus prides himself on recording them in his
work. . . . [But] physically, at least, he was well pro-
portioned. [However] his expression was vacant as is
usual with drunkards, and his speech disordered. His
hair was always dyed and made to shine with gold
dust. He used to singe his hair and beard from fear of
the barber.[14]

In his last years, the emperor seems to have gone partly out
of his mind. Rome was rebaptised *Colonia Commodiana*, and the emperor regarded himself as the reincarnation of Hercules (Hercules
Romanus). He also decided, in January 193, to appear in public as
both consul and gladiator, and Narcissus, an athlete, was taken on to
murder him.

His reign was on the whole a sorry affair, a bad come-down
after those of his distinguished predecessors.

CHAPTER VIII

SEPTIMIUS SEVERUS, CARACALLA *and* ELAGABALUS

SEVERUS (LUCIUS SEPTIMIUS SEVERUS) WAS EMPEROR FROM AD 193 to 211. He was born of an equestrian (knightly) family, with senatorial connections, from Lepcis Magna (Lebda) in Tripolitania. He served with distinction in the army, became consul in 190, and then was appointed to the governorship of Upper Pannonia. In 193, after the assassination of Pertinax and elevation of Didius Julianus to the throne, he was declared emperor at Carnuntum (Petronell), and went into Rome without encountering resistance. He replaced the Praetorians by a new Guard, for which every legionary was eligible, and revived the memory of Pertinax. Then he went to the east, where after a number of engagements he decisively defeated his rival Pescennius Niger on the plain of Issus (194), and then routed Niger's Parthian and other eastern allies. Subsequently he overcame another competitor, Clodius Albinus (to whom he had previously granted the title of Caesar) near Lugdunum (Lyon) (197). But then, after a brief visit to Rome, he moved east again, annexing Osrhoene and Mesopotamia, and spending two years in Syria and Egypt. He spent much of the next six years at Rome (briefly visiting Africa). In

208 he set out, accompanied by his wife and two sons, for Britain. In the hope of suppressing the Caledonians, a Roman invasion of Scotland took place, but Septimius Severus, although he moved far to the north, did not conquer the whole of the country. He withdrew to Eburacum (York), where he died in 211.

Septimius Severus suffered from poor health. While in Egypt, at the turn of the century, he was seriously ill. His illness was called small-pox, but it is not certain, as has been said, that small-pox, as we understand the term, existed at that time.[1] Not long afterwards he experienced the trouble with his feet which went on for the rest of his life. At his Triumph in 208 he was unable to stand up in his chariot, and had to allow his elder son Caracalla to lead the celebrations for his 'victory'. Thereafter, in Britain, his feet became very bad indeed.

As I wrote in *The Severans:*

There is something to be said . . . for the view that the small-pox [or other illness] Septimius caught in Egypt permanently attacked him. In Britain, Septimius had to be carried in a covered litter (and the harsh climate of the country certainly cannot have done him any good). Either he had gout—which was said, in general, to be due to over-indulgence, although Septimius was not accused of this—or he suffered from arthritis. His death was apparently foreseen. However, long before he died, his poor health must have conflicted seriously with his mental alertness and desire for vigorous activity, which his earlier physical

toughness had facilitated. Later on . . . it was his feet
that gave him trouble.[2]

There is little doubt that Severus wanted to conquer the
whole of Britain, of which he went to almost the northern extrem-
ity, and failed to do so because of his poor health, particularly as regards his feet. Instead, having retired from Scotland (after some
quite effective campaigns), he was 'stricken by a very grave illness,
now an old man',[3] and died in 211—at the age of sixty-five, although
he had always had regular habits.

* * *

Caracalla's real name was Marcus Aurelius Antoninus. He was the
elder son of Septimius Severus, who created him Caesar in 196 and
Augustus in 198. His relations with his younger brother Geta, created Augustus in 209, were always precarious, and deteriorated
after the death of Septimius Severus in 211. His widow Julia
Domna prevented a partition of the empire, but in 212 Caracalla
had Geta murdered and became the only emperor. Much loved by
the army, but not by the Senate, in 213 he set out for Germany, and
probably strengthened the fortifications along the frontier of Upper
Germany and Raetia. In 215-216 he proceeded to the east, where
he hoped for vast conquests that would equate him with Alexander
the Great. Massive campaigns followed, but in 217 Caracalla was
murdered near Carrhae (Altibaşak). In 212 he had promulgated an
edict (the *constitutio Antoniniana*) conferring Roman citizenship

upon every community inside the empire, in order to obtain larger revenue from the inheritance tax. Continued inflation resulted in the creation of a new base silver coin worth two *denarii*, known as the *antoninianus*.

Caracalla was always pushed forward by his father, who although he realised his defects possessed, like most emperors, strong dynastic ideas. His younger brother Geta was also pushed forward, although more slowly and later. After the death of Severus, however, Caracalla had Geta murdered, as was stated above.

> For he [Caracalla] was sick not only in body, partly from visible and partly from secret ailments, but in mind as well, suffering from certain distressing visions, and often he thought he was being pursued by his father and by his brother, armed with swords. Therefore he called up spirits to find some remedy against them, among others the spirit of his father and that of Commodus, [who] admitted finally to 'having a malady hard to be cured.' [But] he received no help from Apollo Grannus, nor yet from Aesculapius or Serapis, in spite of his many supplications and his unwearying persistence. For even while abroad he sent to them prayers, sacrifices and votive offerings—and he also went to them himself, hoping to prevail by appearing in person, and did all that devotees are wont to do; but he obtained nothing that contributed to health.[4]

Caracalla's devotion to Aesculapius is confirmed by his appearance on a remarkable series of *sestertii*. This appeal to the gods of health is not new: Aesculapius had already appeared on the coinage of Marcus Aurelius under Antoninus Pius, and had been similarly honoured by Clodius Albinus. But Caracalla's honour to Aesculapius is more distinctive and emphatic. Not that it did him any good. Though what exactly was wrong with him it is difficult to say. Though it is at least certain that he was not only intemperate but had appalling nerves and nervous hallucinations, which made him very restless (not inactive) and all the more emphatic in his distaste for everyone except his soldiers.[5] This meant that he could be judged as a criminal rather than a lunatic.[6]

Mattingly writes,

Along with cruelty and duplicity he had inherited, in an exaggerated form, the religiosity of his family, and his consciousness of his unnatural act [the murder of his brother Geta] afflicted him with superstitious terrors, which drove him to have recourse to dubious sophists, whose prescriptions encouraged an addiction to magical practice. Ill-health contributed to the nervous apprehension in which he lived. His mind became unbalanced. His habitual mood of sullen and suspicious moroseness would sharpen into a craving for bloodshed which the slaughter of the arena could not appease, and which would drive him into a homicidal fury in which revengefulness appears to have been confusedly combined with religious and moral motives.[7]

* * *

One reason for pushing Caracalla forward was the bad health which increasingly engulfed Septimius; but Caracalla, too, was not in good health.

> Caracalla possessed the character of his father (whom, it was said, he at least once intended to kill) . . . in exaggerated and perhaps mentally deranged form. His famous portrait . . . does not lie, or minimise his defects. He showed cruelty and vindictiveness, and was believed to be cowardly as well. His health, like his father's, was poor. . . . But a diagnosis of Caracalla's ailment is impossible—except that he was believed to be impotent. At one time, he was thought to have imported syphilis from the east. . . . On the other side, it does seem possible that the rude remarks about Caracalla's administrative and judicial activities are untrue, or at least exaggerated, and that, instead, although in dubious health, he was pretty methodical, as well as eager to be kept properly informed. He was undoubtedly popular with the soldiers.[8]

* * *

Elagabalus,[9] Roman emperor, 218-222, born Varius Avitus Bassianus, was the son of Julia Soaemias and grand-

son of Julia Maesa, and took his name from the sun-god
of Emesa [Homs], Ela-Gabal, of whom he was hereditary
priest. In his fifteenth year he was saluted Augustus at
Emesa under the title of Marcus Aurelius Antoninus, his
mother alleging that he was the son of Caracalla. After
the defeat of Macrinus he spent the winter at Nicomedia
[Izmit], and only reached Rome in 219.

His chief interest was the advancement of his religion.
Two magnificent temples were built for the Sun-god,
whose midsummer festival was celebrated by his priest
with a ceremonial no less ludicrous than obscene. His
mother attended debates in the Senate, and also
presided over a 'female senate' which formulated rules
of etiquette. Meanwhile positions of responsibility
were given to mere palace servants. In alarm for her
own position and the continuance of the Severan dy-
nasty [Julia] Maesa induced him to adopt his cousin
Alexianus (Severus Alexander) as Caesar (221). Jealousy and intrigue ensued till an opportune bribe by
[Julia] Mamaea, Alexianus's mother, induced the praetorians to murder Elagabalus and his mother.[10]

This is what Hönn added:

He possessed a striking personal beauty which meant
that he contributed spectacular picturesqueness to the

elaborate, jewel-encrusted ritual of his cult. Elagabalus, like Macrinus, merely notified the senators of his accession. They agreed, for fear of the soldiers. And so the new emperor entered Rome, in spring, or July or September, 219. To avoid any suggestion that his origins were exotic, he took and stressed the name of Antoninus, claiming, as was stated, to be the son of Caracalla (to impress the soldiers). Yet he never became very Roman. And his short reign was a joke, a bad joke at that.

Elagabalus was a passive homosexual, and the historians' pages are full of obscene stories about his life. The trouble was that he was extremely young, and saw no reason not to indulge his sexual tendencies to the full. . . . But Julia Maesa tried to make her grandson, the emperor, look respectable by arranging for him to marry at least three successive wives, Julia Paula, Aquilia Severa and Annia Faustina, all of whom, in turn, appeared on coins.[11]

Elagabalus has gone down to history as the ultimate pervert. Admittedly some of the stories that are told about him are possibly inventions: how did the historians really know what was going on, at this supreme level? This, for example, is what Dio Cassius recorded:

He used his body both for doing and allowing many strange things, which no one could endure to tell or hear of; but his most conspicuous acts, which it would be impossible to conceal, were the following. He would go to the taverns by night, wearing a wig, and there ply the trade of a female huckster. He frequented the notorious brothels, drove out the prostitutes, and played the prostitute himself. Finally, he set aside a room in the palace and there committed his indecencies, always standing nude at the door of his room, as the harlots do, and shaking the curtain which hung from gold rings, while in a soft and melting voice he solicited the passers-by . . . he had, besides, a favourite 'husband', whom he wished to appoint Caesar for that very reason.[12]

And this is what the *Historia Augusta* adds:

Who could tolerate an emperor who indulged in unnatural lusts of every kind, when not even a beast of this sort could be tolerated? And even at Rome he did nothing but send out agents in search for those who had particularly large organs and bring them to the palace in order that he might enjoy their vigour. Moreover, he used to have the story of Paris played in his house, and he himself would take the role of Venus, and suddenly drop his clothing to the ground and fall naked on his knees, one hand on his breast, the other before his private parts, his buttocks projecting mean-

while and thrust back in front of his partner in de-
pravity. . . . [He deemed] it the chief enjoyment of his
life to appear fit and worthy to arouse the lusts of the
greatest number.[13]

As stated above, he clearly was a passive homosexual, and this
aroused mirth and hostility, and must be considered a form of ill-
health which handicapped a ruler. Even Julius Caesar had been
laughed at all his life because, when young, he was supposed to have
been a boy-friend of King Nicomedes IV Philopator of Bithynia. To
be an active homosexual was quite different: the popular emperor
Trajan was one, and the Romans considered that bisexuality, on such
a basis, was perfectly legitimate. I have met with the same reaction
in African and Asian countries today. The goings-on of Elagabalus,
however, as a passive homosexual, seemed quite intolerable, especially as many of his thoughts and actions were un-Roman—indeed,
it may well be that this is what annoyed the Romans most—and it
was because he was a passive homosexual that his grandmother Julia
Maesa provided him with three successive wives, one of them,
Aquilia Severa, he married twice. Heaven knows what went on in
the bedroom. At any rate here was a form of ill-health which influenced the whole empire, and did harm.

After the Severans—the last of them was Elagabalus's cousin
and successor Severus Alexander—the empire seemed to plunge
into virtual chaos, from which it was gradually rescued, as we shall
now see.

CHAPTER IX

DIOCLETIAN *and* CONSTANTINE

A FTER THE COLLAPSE OF THE SEVERANS (235) IT SEEMED UNLIKELY that the Roman empire, its northern and eastern frontiers imperilled, would survive. But it did, owing to a series of impressive military emperors, of whom Claudius II Gothicus (268-270) and Aurelian (270-275) were outstanding. We hear nothing about their health. Then Diocletian (284-305) reorganised the empire thoroughly, under the system of a Tetrarchy, consisting of two Augusti and two Caesars.

A. H. M. Jones writes of Diocletian,

> Gaius Aurelius Valerius Diocletianus, originally named Diocles, [was] a Dalmatian of low birth who rose to be commander of the emperor Numerian's bodyguard. Chosen by the army near Nicomedia [Izmit] in November AD 284 to avenge his master's death, he struck down the praetorian prefect, Aper. He then marched westwards to defeat Numerian's brother, Carinus, at Margus (on the Dacian frontier, early 285). He at once chose Maximian, an old comrade, to be his Caesar and sent him to Gaul to suppress the Bacaudae

(insurgent peasants). Quickly victorious, Maximian was raised to the rank of Augustus early in 286. The frontier situation was serious. . . . In view of the many difficulties of the government, Diocletian in 295 established his famous 'tetrarchy'. Himself Augustus in the east, he took Galerius to be his Caesar, while to Maximian, Augustus in the west, was assigned Constantius Chlorus. . . . [After severe fighting in Mesopotamia], in 303 Diocletian visited Rome for the first time, to celebrate his *vicennalia*. A collapse in health the following year almost cost him his life, and on 1st May 305 he abdicated with Maximian.[1]

This was the first abdication of an emperor in Roman history. The reference to Diocletian's 'collapse in health' is undoubtedly true, although we do not exactly know what was the matter with him, other than the fact that 'he suffered a very severe and prolonged illness'.[2] Mattingly suggested that 'he suffered some form of nervous breakdown, which incapacitated him for all public duties'.[3] Anyway, this is the only case of an abdication in imperial history, and it was caused by ill-health. Its effects were enormous; the first result was the break-down of the Tetrarchy.

* * *

For it did not survive, and Constantine I the Great emerged as the single ruler of the whole empire in 324.

Constantine I (the Great) (Flavius Valerius Constantinus)[4] was born in about AD 285 and died in 337. He was the son of Constantius I Chlorus and Helena. His birthplace was Naissus (Niş). He was at the court of Diocletian when he abdicated in 305. In 306, when Constantius I died at Eburacum (York), Constantine was proclaimed Augustus by the troops and was made Caesar by Galerius. At the Conference of Carnuntum (Petronell) in 308 Constantine was called upon to disclaim the title of Augustus and be content with that of Caesar, under Licinius. In 311, when Galerius died, Constantine and Maxentius sought the backing of Licinius and Maximinus II respectively. In 312 Constantine invaded Italy, fought successfully at Augusta Taurinorum (Turin) and Verona, defeated and killed Maxentius at the Milvian Bridge (Ponte Molle) outside Rome and entered the city. In 313 Licinius married Constantia, the sister of Constantine, but relations soon worsened. In 314 or 316 Constantine defeated him twice, and gained territory as far as Thrace. In 324, again defeated several times, Licinius abdicated and was executed, leaving Constantine as sole ruler. He reorganised the administration, turned Byzantium into Constantinople, gave privileges to the Christians, and repulsed the Goths (332). But he ordered the execution of his wife Fausta and his eldest son Crispus (326), leaving the empire to his three other sons and the two sons of his half-brother.

Constantine 'the Great' fought the battle of the Milvian Bridge in 312, in which he defeated and killed the rival (pagan) emperor Maxentius, as a result of a dream. It was said that he had had visions before, but whether he did or not there is no reason to doubt

that during the night that immediately preceded the battle he had
a dream which not only encouraged him to fight and win the battle
but turned him towards Christianity. What apparently happened
according to Franz was this.

> When he was asleep, the Christ of God appeared to
> him and he brought with him the sign which had ap-
> peared in the sky. . . . In the morning he told his
> friends of this extraordinary experience. . . . It was ap-
> parently based on a *real* dream, and not a dubious vi-
> sionary experience. . . . In such circumstances it was
> natural that the dreamers, on awakening, should sum-
> mon their advisers and try to find out from them what
> the dream had meant. And that is no doubt what Con-
> stantine did. . . . What Lactantius heard was that God
> had told Constantine, in this nocturnal visitation, to
> inscribe the sublime sign of God on his soldiers'
> shields before engaging the enemy. And when Con-
> stantine woke up at dawn on 28 October, we are told,
> he informed his friends of this portentous message. . . .
> The immediate result of Constantine's dream . . .was
> that he was said to have decided to inscribe the *Chi-
> Rho*, interpreted not only as a symbol of forthcoming
> victory, but as a Christian symbol as well, upon the
> shields of his soldiers, before the decisive Battle of the
> Milvian Bridge against Maxentius. . . . Very possibly,
> the emperor's dream, on that night before the engage-

ment, was directed and shaped by his Christian advis-
ers. But he had the dream all the same.[5]

That dreams prophesied the future was very widely held in
the ancient world, as indeed it still is today.[6]

I would repeat here, in connection with dreams, what I said
about astrology in Chapter II. It may seem strange to some that
dreams are included as one of the aspects of the sickness of the Caesars. And indeed, if anyone finds this intolerable, let him or her skip
the present passage. Nevertheless, I do persist in regarding dreams
as one of the aspects of the sickness of the Caesars. True, millions of
other people, too, believed in them; and there were learned or rather
pseudo-learned writings on the subject. Innumerable people today
believe in the prophetic authority in dreams (although there are also
those who say 'dreams go by opposites'). So they, too, suffer from
this kind of mental sickness. For sickness, in my view, it is: it is totally wrong, and if believed in will cause people to take peculiar and
often wholly erroneous actions.

Divination by means of dreams, a recognised art in ancient times, was called oneiromancy (from the Greek
oneiron, 'dream'), and for the unsophisticated, and not
so unsophisticated, in all ages dreams have possessed
significance of a sort that enabled the oneiromancer to
have his art taken seriously. Even in the second half of
the 20th century so-called dream books are still pur-
chased by the credulous for the purpose of ascertaining

the presumed prophetic meaning of given dream sym-
bols. . . . [The] unreality of dream events is . . . suggested by the derivation of the word 'dream', which is
traced through the Anglo-Saxon to the root meaning
of the modern German word *Traum*: this is in turn related to the German word *trüger*, which means 'to deceive' . . . the idea of deception [is thus] implicit in the
earliest root meaning of the word.[7]

The ancient world, and especially the world of Constantine's
epoch, was as credulous of significant nocturnal dreams as it was of
other kinds of visions. 'It is to dreams', wrote Tertullian, 'that the
majority of humankind owe their knowledge of God.' Artemidorus
of Ephesus devoted a study to the subject, the *Oneirocriticon*. Divine
powers were believed to visit people very often in their dreams and
give them messages, and this was thought to apply particularly to
great and powerful men. Thus an angel was said to have appeared in
a dream to Licinius, and Constantine himself was said to have seen
and talked with God in dreams, as part of his lifelong relationship
with the supernatural.

As L. Edelstein said:

As regards mantic dreams, most of the physicians of
all centuries admit their reality; they acknowledge
even their divine character. . . . The Methodists are the
only physicians who apparently do not believe in divine dreams; they never mention them. . . . But in

general physicians, as scientists, believe in mira-
cles. . . . The Methodists . . . were the only physicians
who objected to the possibility of divine interference.[8]

The Methodists were right; but the fact that Constantine
shared this widespread view, this form of mental ill-health, is hardly
surprising. It merely indicates what one might expect: that this particular sort of sickness was extended to emperors. In this particular
case, however, it directed and changed the whole course of the future.

EPILOGUE

ONE THING THAT HAS EMERGED CLEARLY FROM THIS STUDY IS that the sickness of the Caesars was far from trivial, but had profound and long-term effects. For example, Aurelius would probably have invaded Germany if he had not suffered from bad health, and Septimius Severus would have conquered the whole of Britain. Moreover, the Tetrarchy would not have collapsed without the sickness of Diocletian who had created it; and, also, his is the only abdication—due principally to ill-health—in Roman history. Constantine would not have fought and won the battle of the Milvian Bridge against Maxentius, and would not, therefore, have instituted Christianity at Rome if he had not been encouraged to by a dream. For belief in dreams was one of the forms of sickness from which the Romans suffered, another being the belief in astrology and horoscopes, which one ruler after another evinced. Augustus, for example, was a keen believer in astrology, but he is chiefly notable in the context of the present book as someone who consistently fought against the ill-health which continually oppressed him, and who did so successfully, living to what, in Roman times,

was considered quite an old age. Before him, however, Julius Caesar seems already to have made astute political use of his own sickness, which consisted of a tendency to epilepsy—deeply revered as
a gift of the gods.

NOTES

Introduction

1. F. F. Cartwright, *Disease and History,* (1972), pp. 1ff.; *cf.* C. Roberts and K. Manchester (eds.), *The Archaeology of Disease* (2nd ed., 1997); R. Jackson, *Doctors and Diseases in the Roman Empire* (1991, 1995).

2. *Cf.* A. Essex, *Cäsar und die Julisch-Claudischen Kaiser in biologischen-ärtzlichen Blicks* (1955); A. Demandt, *Das Privatleben der römischen Kaiser* (1991); G. E. W. Wolstenholme & C. M. O'Connor, CIBA Foundation Symposium on Medical Biology and Etruscan Origins (1959); R. Jackson, *Doctors and Diseases in the Roman Empire* (1991, 1995).

3. Suetonius, *Domitian* 21; *cf.* I. Lissner, *The Caesars: Might and Madness* (1958), p. 172; S. Dill, *Roman Society from Nero to Marcus Aurelius* (1905), p. 40.

4. *Cf.* S. Dill, *Roman Society in the Last Century of the Western World,* p. 452.

5. It must not be forgotten that there were considerable irrational elements in society. Astrology, and dreams, are among the results, as we shall see.

6. E.g. Ritschmer, *Great Men: Psychoanalytic Studies* (1956); R. S.
    Stevenson, *Famous Illnesses in History* (1962); G. E. Mastier,
    Disease and Destiny (1962); De Mause, *The New Psychohistory*
    (1975); Prisco, *An Introduction to Psychohistory* (1980); Strozier,
    The Leader: Psychohistorical Essays (1985); Weigall, *Leaders
    under Stress* (1985); B. E. Park, *The Impact of Illness on World
    Leaders* (1986). 'It is to my sickness', said Nietzsche, 'that I
    owe a *higher* health.'

Chapter I: Julius Caesar

1. M. Gelzer, *Caesar: Politician and Statesman* (1968), p. 326 n.1,
    who gives much modern evidence. We do not know the
    names of Caesar's doctors. His epilepsy (if this was his trou-
    ble) evidently did not interfere very much with his work.
    These introductions to the emperors' lives are mostly taken
    from the *Oxford Classical Dictionary,* 2nd ed., 1970. There
    have been new editions now.

2. Plutarch, *Caesar,* 17.3; *cf.* Suetonius, *Augustus* 25.86. The
    hereditary nature of Caesar's epilepsy, if that was his trouble,
    has been widely discussed. *Cf.* also A. Essex, *Cäsar und die
    Julisch-Claudischen Kaiser in biologischen-ärtzlichen Blicks*
    (1955), p. 25.

3. *Cf.* C. Meier, *Caesar: A Biography* (1982), p. 423.

4. The ensuing massacre was largely Caesar's fault, Gelzer, *ibid.,*
    pp. 26f. n. 3. But Gelzer disbelieves in the whole incident
    quoted above, *ibid.,* pp. 268 n. 6.

5. Dio, *Epit.,* XLIII. 24 commented on the public shock caused
    by killing other Romans.

6. O. Temkin, *The Falling Sickness* (1985).

7. Dio, *Epit.,* XLIV. 8 (tr. E. Cary).

8. Suetonius, *Caesar,* 78 (tr. R. Graves, M. Grant).

9. Gelzer, *op. cit.,* p. 317.

10. Plutarch, *Caesar.*

11. *Ibid.*

12. Balsdon, *Julius Caesar and Rome* (1967), p. 54, is doubtful whether Caesar was really ill at the time.

13. *Cf.* Meier, *op. cit.,* p. 478.

14. Caesar himself was apparently prepared for a sudden and early end.

15. Plutarch, *Caesar, cf.* M. Grant, *Julius Caesar,* p. 217.

Chapter II: Augustus

1. Suetonius, *Augustus,* 98f. (tr. R. Graves, M. Grant).

2. J. B. Firth, *Augustus Caesar* (1902), pp. 346f.

3. A. Massie, *Augustus* (1986), p. 79.

4. Suetonius, *op. cit.,* 80. Suetonius also adds that he had stomach trouble, and was once ill when he held the Games.

5. J. B. Firth, *loc. cit.*

6. For the significance attached to dreams, *cf.* Chapter 10. Octavian attached great important to this one.

7. M. Grant, *The Twelve Caesars* (1975), p. 71. Octavian fell sick and was left behind at Dyrrhachium (Dürres), while Antony

marched towards Philippi. At the First Battle of Philippi, according to one account, he was carried along the ranks in a litter, and went round shaking hands (of which he was proud enough to record the incident in his memoir). *Cf.* Appian, *Romaika,* IV, 108, V, 11.

8. The Cantabrian War gave Augustus abscesses of the liver. He narrowly escaped death from lightning, which gave him a permanent fear of storms.

9. Plutarch, *Caesar, cf.* above.

10. Augustus handed over the command to a *legatus*; and was at first too ill to go to Rome.

11. Dio, *Epit.,* LVIII. 50.

12. J. B. Firth, *op. cit.*, pp. 174f. What was wrong with him? Perhaps catarrh.

13. *Cf.* Suetonius, *op. cit.*, 59. The cold-water treatment of Antonius Musa. This was contrary to all Roman medical practice. But Augustus conferred civil immunity on doctors. For the medicine of the early empire, *cf.* J. Scarborough, M. Grant and R. Kitzinger (eds), *Civilization of the Ancient Mediterranean,* pp. 1237, 1241ff., 1248.

14. J. B. Firth, *op. cit.*, p. 175.

15. Augustus was ill again in 6 BC and AD 13. On hearing of the defeat and death of Varus at the hands of the Germans in the Teutoburg Forest, he may have had a temporary nervous breakdown. He used to go to the house of Maecenas when he was unwell.

16. Suetonius, *op. cit.*, 98f. *Cf.* M. Grant, *op. cit.*, pp. 98ff.

17. *Ibid.*, 74.

18. *Ibid., Tiberius,* 62, 69, *cf.* Tacitus, *Annals,* VI, 24. The emperors shared this taste with many other people, including many of the best minds of the ancient world. Many preferred the determinism of the astrologers to the weight of personal responsibility.

19. There were nine expulsions between 130 BC and AD 93, and many subsequently.

20. Sir Winston Churchill, when Prime Minister during the war, had to ask newspaper editors to silence their astrologers, whose predictions, according to him, weakened the war effort.

21. H. Mattingly and E. A. Sydenham, *The Roman Imperial Coinage,* I (1923), pp. 48f. Dio XLIX.43 tells of the expulsion in 33 BC, by Agrippa.

22. H. Mattingly, *The Coins of the Roman Empire in the British Museum,* I (1923), pp. cxf. His references are to J. B. Smyly, *Hermathena* (1912), pp. 150ff.; A. E. Housman, *Manilius: Astronomicon,* IV, 776. Mattingly also points to a coin (*op. cit.*, p. 62, no. 349) which shows, with the capricorn, Aurora, hovering in the air—apparently a reference to the hour of Augustus's birth.

Chapter III: Tiberius

1. I. Lissner, *The Caesars: Might and Madness* (1958).

2. A. Massie, *Tiberius,* (1996), p. 240. *Cf.* also F. Wiederseck, *Das Cäsarenwahnsinn der Julisch-Claudischen Imperatorfamilie geschildert an den Kaisern Tiberius, Caligula, Claudius, Nero;*

M. Baar, *Das Bilo der Kaisers Tiberius bei Tacitus, Suetonius und Cassius Dio* (1990).

3.   Tacitus, *Annals*, IV, 57.

4.   *Ibid.*, VI, 22.

5.   *Ibid.*, VI, 51; endlessly debated.

Chapter IV: Caligula

1.   C. Quidde, *Caligula: eine Studie der römischen Casarenwahnsinn* (1894) (an attack on Wilhelm II); A. A. Barrett, *Caligula; the Corruption of Power* (1909, 1993); H. Sachs, *Bubi: Die Lebensgeschichte der Caligula* (1930), etc; Caligula's doctor was Halcyon. *Cf.* also A. Demandt, *Das Privatleben der römischen Kaiser* (1996).

2.   E.g. R. Porter, *A Social History of Madness* (1983), V. H. H. Green, *The Madness of Kings: Personal Trauma and the Fate of Nations* (1984), etc.

3.   Suetonius, *Gaius*, 508.

4.   R. Porter, *op. cit.*, pp. 1–6.

5.   D. D. Hook, *Madmen of History* (1976), preface; *cf.* V. H. H. Green, *op. cit.*

6.   Suetonius, *Gaius*, 50f., 56. But the sources are very unreliable, being hostile, prejudiced, anecdotal and trivial.

7.   Baring-Gould, *The Tragedy of the Caesars*, pp. 324f.

8.   A. A. Massie, *Caligula*, p. 131.

9. M. P. Charlesworth, *Cambridge Ancient History,* X (1934), p. 632.

10. A. Garzetti, *From Tiberius to the Antonines* (1974, 1960). Caligula was young, sadistic, extravagant and self-indulgent; he was quite unprepared for rulership and its enormous demands.

11. The relations of Caligula with the Jews are discussed by M. Grant, *The Jews in the Roman World* (1973), pp. 120f. Reference might also be made to modern African tyrants such as Idi Amin or the Emperor Bokassa, who likewise enjoyed unrestrained rule.

12. J. P. V. D. Balsdon, *The Emperor Gaius* (1934), pp. 213ff. Caligula began to feel entitled to divine honours, or at least he was unprecedentedly favourable to imperial absolutism— a return, it may be called to Caesarism—perhaps under the inspiration of his grandfather Antony: or his mother Antonia's Egyptian slaves, since he was undoubtedly under the influence of oriental ideas. But he had a highly developed sense of humour, and remained popular (except in the Senate, to which he was hostile); but he felt threatened, perhaps with good reason. His health remained uncertain; he was indisposed even on the day when he was murdered.

13. A. A. Barrett, *op. cit.,* p. 213.

14. M. Grant, *The Twelve Caesars* (1975, 1996), pp. 11ff.

15. J. P. V. D. Balsdon, *op. cit.,* pp. 212f., *cf.* pp. 35f.

Chapter V: Claudius

1. *Cf.* T. de C. Ruth, *The Problem of Claudius* (1916); M. Scramuzza, *The Emperor Claudius* (1940); B. Levick, *Claudius* (1990). Robert Graves, *I Claudius* and *Claudius the God* (1934), gives a fine imaginative picture of the man and his reign.

2. Suetonius, *Claudius,* 34f., 40.

3. *Cf.* M. Grant, *The Twelve Caesars,* (1975, 1996), p. 129.

4. M. Grant, *op. cit*; *cf.* V. M. Scramuzza, *op. cit.*, p. 35. Doctors say that cerebral palsy is not likely. Infantile paralysis may account for his limp and stutter. But motor paralysis and paralytic diplegia have been suggested; also a premature birth and acute viral infection. There was an Arab tradition of Claudius's interest in epilepsy and its cures. Perhaps there was an inherited neuropathy. Claudius's doctor Gaius Stertimius Xenophon, sent to him by his wife Agrippina the younger, was the first to be called *archiatros*. During the illness Claudius went to bathe at Sinuessa (Suetonius, *op. cit.* 54).

5. V. M. Scramuzza, *op. cit.*, pp. 310ff.

6. T. de C. Ruth, *op. cit.*, pp. 127f, 131, 133f., 137.

7. Suetonius, *op. cit.*, 4.

8. Nature had begun him, she said, but had failed to complete the task.

9. Suetonius, *op. cit.* It has been argued that his defects were exaggerated.

10. These disturbed him so much that he thought of suicide, Suetonius, *op. cit.*, 31.

11. At the time of his death he was torpid or drunk.

12. *Cf.* Scramuzza, *op. cit.*, p. 37, 44, 237 n. 112.

13. Suetonius, *Galba*, 21.

14. *Ibid., Otho*, 12.

15. *Ibid., Vitellius*, 13.

16. *Ibid., Vespasian*, 24.

Chapter VI: Domitian and After

1. The doctor of Titus was Apollinaris.

2. *Cf.* Pliny the younger, *Panegyricus*, 48.4; Suetonius, *Domitian*, 4; Tacitus, *Agricola*, 45.3.

3. M. Grant, *The Twelve Caesars* (1975, 1996), pp. 243f.

4. Suetonius, *Domitian*, 14.

5. *Ibid.*, 3; *cf.* M. Grant, *op. cit.*, p. 244, S. Gsell, *Essai sur la régne de l'empéreur Domitian*, 3. P. Southern, *Domitian: Tragic Tyrant* (1997).

6. Suetonius, *op. cit.*, 15; on astrology *cf.* above, Chapter II.

7. R. P. Longden, *Cambridge Ancient History*, XI (1936), p. 190.

8. Dio, *Epit.*, LXVIII, 1.3.

9. *Ibid.*, 33. Trajan's doctor was Statilius Crito. According to

J. Bennett, *Trajan: Optimus Princeps* (1996), Trajan has been too favourably regarded.

10. *Ibid.,* LXIX.7.

11. *Ibid.,* 17, 20, 22.

12. B. W. Henderson, *The Life and Principate of the Emperor Hadrian* (1923), p. 264.

13. Dio, *Epit.,* LXIX, 22.4; *cf.* I. Lissner, *The Caesars: Might and Madness* (1958), p. 19.

14. *Historia Augusta, Antoninus Pius,* 13.1.

Chapter VII: Marcus Aurelius and Commodus

1. Dio, *Epit.,* LXXII, 6.3–4, 34.2, 36.2–3. *Cf.* M. Grant, *The Antonines* (1994), p. 56. Winter campaigning in the north had taken its toll. 'I had no needs', said Aurelius himself, 'but my wretched body had perhaps': *cf.* Julian, *Caesars,* pp. 134f. Aurelius often refers to his health in letters to Fronto. Sleeping was a serious problem for him.

2. Galen, *Prognosis,* XI, *cf.* M. Grant, *op. cit.,* p. 57.

3. Marcus Aurelius, *Meditations,* 7.64, 33, 6.33; *cf.* A. Birley, *Marcus Aurelius: A Biography* (1966, 1987), pp. 179 n. 41, 216 nn. 11f.

4. Marcus Aurelius, *op. cit.,* I.8.17. Is this 'Chrysa' a town in the Troad. M. Grant, *op. cit.,* pp. 56, 182.

5. M. Grant, *op. cit.,* pp. 56f.

6. It is uncertain if Aurelius died at Sirmium (Sremska Mitro-

vica) or Vindobona (Vienna). It was reported that he had stopped eating and drinking, because he was eager to die. He had been seriously ill when visiting Pannonia.

7. A. Birley, *op. cit.*, p. 179.

8. T. W. Africa, *Journal of the History of Ideas,* XXI (1961), pp. 97ff.

9. A. Prantera, *On This Side of the Moon* (1992), pp. 164f.

10. Galen, *On Antidotes,* I, 1–5.

11. F. F. Cartwright, *Disease and History* (1972), p. 116, *cf.* pp. 13ff.

12. M. Grant, *op. cit.*, p. 32, *cf.* R. P. Duncan-Jones, *The Impact of the Antonine Plague,* (*Journal of Roman Archaeology* XI, 1996, pp. 108ff.).

13. Aurelius possibly felt qualms about this. On Roman imperial successors, *cf.* Tacitus, *Histories,* I, 16. R. Mellor, *Tacitus* (1992), p. 102.

14. M. Grant, *op. cit.*, p. 68 n. 8. Commodus is reported to have said that his chief desire was good health. *Historia Augusta, Commodus,* 28.

Chapter VIII: Septimius Severus, Caracalla and Elagabalus

1. Many people went through life untested, and without even realising that they suffered from the disease—if it existed. C. Roberts and K. Manchester (eds.), *The Archaeology of Disease* (2nd ed., 1997) call it 'the scourge of antiquity' (p. 125), but its ancient history is very disputable (*cf.* p. 133).

2. M. Grant, *The Severans* (1996), pp. 19, 13. *Cf.* A. Birley, *Septimius Severus* (1971), pp. 253f., and *Historia Augusta, Septimius Severus,* 18. Gout, as understood in the ancient world, was not necessarily what it is today; but for the condition see *Gout: A Handbook for Patients* (Arthritis & Rheumatism Council, 1977) C. Roberts and K. Manchester (eds.), *ibid.,* p. 235 (S. V. Feet), *cf.* pp. 122f.

3. *Historia Augusta, op. cit.,* p. 19.

4   *Ibid.*

5. M. Grant, *The Severans* (1996), pp. 19, 21; *cf.* O. T. Schulz, *Der römische Kaiser Caracalla: Genie, Wahnsinn oder Verbrechen* (1909); J. Nollé, *Die Krankheit des Kaisers Caracallas.* Caracalla had already been ill in 205, Dio, *Epit., LXXVII.* 2.2, but he rapidly declined after the murder of his brother Geta, and lost interest in governing the empire. He suffered from loss of blood, and could not command the troops (much as he loved them) in summer 215. He was greedy about food and drink, and was said to have become impotent. But he had a sharp tongue, and was naturally shrewd.

6. Dio, *Epit., LXXVIII.* 15.5f., *cf. Historia Augusta, Caracalla,* 5.3.

7. H. Mattingly, *Coins of the Roman Empire in the British Museum,* V (1950), p. 485 no. 278 etc. He also turned to the Punic god of healing, Eshmun, *ibid.,* p. clxxiv.

8. Dio, *Epit., LXXVII.* 20.2. He aimed at becoming a new Alexander the Great.

9. *Cf.* J. Nollé, *Die Krankheit des Kaisers Caracallas* (1996), pp. 27-33.

10.   S. N. Miller, *Cambridge Ancient History,* Vol. XII (1956), p. 44.

11.   *Cf.* K. Hönn, *Untersuchungen zu der Vita des Heliogabalus und des Severus Alexander* (1911).

12.   M. Grant, *The Severans* (1996), pp. 24f.

13.   Dio, *Epit.,* LXXX. 2ff., 14, 1.

Chapter IX: Diocletian and Constantine

1.   A. H. M. Jones, *Encyclopaedia Britannica* (1971 ed.), II, 7, p. 461.

2.   H. Mattingly, *Cambridge Ancient History,* XII (1956), p. 340; *cf.* also p. 668 for supplementary reasons. All M. Cary can say (M. Cary and H. H. Scullard, *A History of Rome,* 3rd ed., 1975, p. 520) is that 'he was getting old and feeling the burden of rule', but surely he was actually ill, as R. Hanslik, *Der Kleine Pauly,* II (1979), p. 39, realises.

3.   *Cf.* A. Birley, *Lives of the Later Caesars* (1976) (*Historia Augusta*).

4.   M. Grant, *The Emperor Constantine* (1993), pp. 140ff., 144f.

5.   *Cf.* M. Franz, *Dreams* (1901); F. Cox Miller, *Dreams in Late Antiquity* (1994); M. Drabble, *The Gates of Ivory* (1991); B. O. States, *Seeing in the Dark* (1996); B. O. States, *Readings in the Dark* (1997), etc.

6.   D. B. Klein, *Encyclopaedia Britannica* (1971 ed.), VII, p. 665.

7.   S. Dill, *Roman Society from Nero to Marcus Aurelius* (1905), pp. 467ff., is very (and quite rightly) hostile to the methods

and conclusions of Artemidorus; and Cicero, *De Divinatione,*
II, 150, criticises ancient beliefs in dreams. So had Penelope,
in the *Odyssey,* XIX, 560ff.

8.   L. Edelstein, *Ancient Medicine* (ed. O. & C. L. Temkin), 1994
      (1967), pp. 241ff.

APPENDICES

LIST *of* EMPERORS

30 BC–AD 14	Augustus
AD 14–37	Tiberius
37–41	Caligula (Gaius)
41–54	Claudius
54–67	Nero
68–69	Galba
69	Otho
69	Vitellius
69–79	Vespasian
79–81	Titus
81–96	Domitian
96–98	Nerva
98–117	Trajan

117–138	Hadrian
138–161	Antoninus Pius
{ 161–180	Marcus Aurelius
{ 161–169	Lucius Verus
180–192	Commodus
193	Pertinax
193	Didius Julianus
193–211	Septimius Severus
{ 211–217	Caracalla
{ 211–212	Geta
{ 217–218	Macrinus
218–222	Elagabalus
222–235	Severus Alexander
235–238	Maximinus I Thrax
{ 238	Gordian I
{ 238	Gordian II
{ 238	Balbinus
{ 238	Pupienus
238–244	Gordian III
244–249	Philip
249–251	Trajanus Decius

251–253	Trebonianus Gallus
253	Aemilian
{ 253–260	Valerian
253–268	Gallienus
268–270	Claudius II Gothicus
270–275	Aurelian
275–276	Tacitus
276	Florian
276–282	Probus
282–283	Carus
{ 283–284	Carinus
283–284	Numerian
{ 284–305	Diocletian
286–305, 307–308	Maximian
{ 305-306	Constantius I
305-311	Galerius
306–307	Severus II
306–312	Maxentius
{ 306–337	Constantine I 'the Great'
306–324	Licinius I

〉

The western and eastern empires finally divided in 364, and the western empire ceased to exist (under German pressure) in 476, though the eastern empire (henceforward known as the Byzantine) continued to survive—with an intermission in the thirteenth century—until 1453.

GENEALOGICAL TABLES

1. The Julio-Claudians

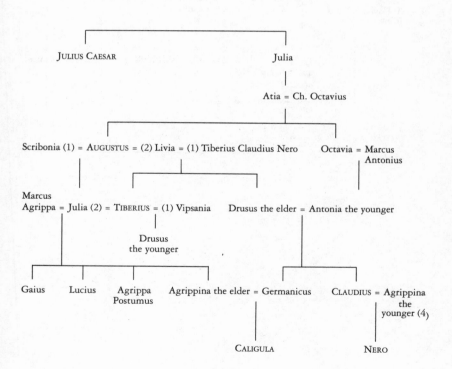

2. The Flavians

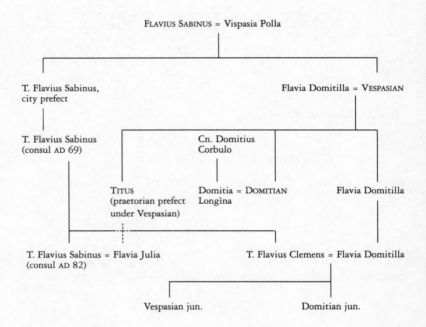

3. *The Adoptive and Antonine Emperors*

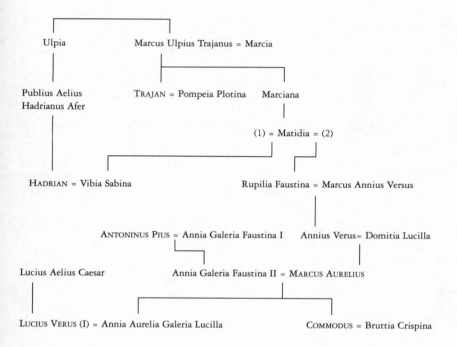

4. *The House of Severus*

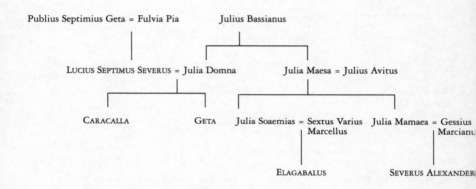

5. *The Tetrarchy and the House of Constantine*

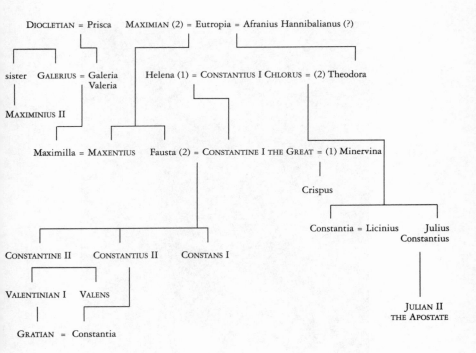

1. Julius Caesar

Green diabase portrait of Julius Caesar. Berlin, Altes Museum.
Courtesy of Foto Marburg/Art Resource, NY.

Julius Caesar

Caesar was one of the most remarkable men who have ever lived: of exceptional brain-power, extremely determined, and a general of quite remarkable quality. He was also amazingly hard-working, and drove himself extremely hard. But he suffered from a disease described by the ancients as epilepsy—and perhaps belonging to one of the numerous branches of which that illness is now believed to exist. He also set, or followed, a precedent by utilising this ill-health for personal and political purposes. Thus he cited it, at Thapsus—perhaps quite rightly—as a reason for not actually participating in the battle, which he obviously did not want to do since it would result in the deaths of many Roman citizens, on the other side in this merciless civil war. And then again he gave his ill-health as the reason why, himself the dictator, he did not stand up when an important delegation of senators visited him to confer honours. This went down badly, because it seemed like an arrogant gesture prompted not by ill-health but by a desire to show his own autocracy and put the Senate in its place. But Caesar asserted that he had remained seated because his health required this.

2. Augustus

Bust of Augustus. Musei Capitolini; Rome, Italy.
Courtesy of Alinari/Art Resource, NY.

Augustus

Augustus was an example of a man who overcame ill-health for many years and achieved mighty things. He lived to the age of nearly seventy-eight, which was a lot at that time. He had been scoffed at for his failure to act as an effective colleague to Mark Antony at the battle of Philippi (42 BC), and in 23 BC he made use of a serious illness to establish his final autocratic, but seemingly non-autocratic, constitution, involving continuation and heredity. But he survived, and went on living for thirty-seven years. He was a great hypochondriac and took his ill-health very seriously.

3. Augustus

The Battle of Actium; portraits of Augustus. Roman cameos. Kunsthistorisches
Museum, Vienna, Austria. Courtesy of Alinari/Art Resource, NY.

Augustus (continued)

The *capricorn* which figures so largely on Augustus's coinage is taken from his horoscope, and shows how strongly he, like other emperors, was influenced by astrology, which is a totally false pseudo-science, and in fact a form of ill-health.

4. Tiberius

Bust of Emperor Tiberius. Museo Archeologico Nazionale, Naples, Italy.
Courtesy of Alinari/Art Resource, NY.

Tiberius

Tiberius made an extraordinary decision, and influenced the course of history, when he left Rome permanently for Capreae (Capri) in AD 26. Various reasons have been put forward for this remarkable decision, and among them—which has not, I think, been given sufficient weight—is the skin-disease on his face which must have discouraged this retiring and sensitive man from meeting senators and others. There were, of course, other reasons for his retirement as well, but this physical cause should not be underestimated.

5. Gaius (Caligula)

Bust of Caligula.
Courtesy of Alinari/Art Resource, NY.

Gaius (Caligula)

Gaius (Caligula) had had a curious and deleterious upbringing, but was still quite a young man when he became ruler of the whole world from the Atlantic to the Euphrates. Most young men whom we know would become pretty unhinged by such an occurrence, and this was no doubt the experience of Caligula, helped on by an attack of serious illness. He clearly believed that the regime carefully drawn up and built up by Augustus was bogus, and that the empire was, in fact, under an autocrat, namely himself. And he became, or was, extremely high-handed and cruel. But was he bad, or mad? Opinions have differed; and indeed opinions differ even today about whether a man who commits murder is bad or mad. One can tell to what extent opinions differ by noting the very varied decisions on the subject by judges in the courts, who sometimes send evidently dislocated murderers to prisons and sometimes to hospitals. The example of Caligula is valuable.

6. Claudius

Portrait bust of Emperor Claudius. Musei Capitolini, Rome, Italy.
Courtesy of Alinari/Art Resource, NY.

Claudius

There was evidently something wrong with Claudius from a physical viewpoint, as abundant evidence of his appearance makes clear; despite the attempts of imperial sculptors and coin-engravers to make him look like a god. Indeed, in his early youth his elders all thought he was deficient. Yet when he came to the throne he was on the whole not too bad a ruler, despite a tendency to drink and, as time went on, excessive reliance on women and freedmen.

7. *Galba*

Bust of Galba. Musei Capitolini, Rome, Italy.
Courtesy of Alinari/Art Resource, NY.

Galba

Galba was rather old, by Roman standards, when he came to the throne, and his physical condition was by no means good. If it had been better, he might have survived the attacks which very soon brought him down.

8. *Domitian*

Portrait bust of Domitian. Musei Capitolini, Rome, Italy.
Courtesy of Alinari/Art Resource, NY.

Domitian

Domitian was the second son of Vespasian, but by no means as pleasant a character. In some ways, he was not a bad emperor, but he was ruthless and cruel. It is possible to detect in him a considerable streak of sadism, and he was sensitive, with perilous results, about his baldness. He had other physical problems as well. But his main trouble was probably fear, which made him a very nervous person, who always suspected the worst, with serious effects on his policies.

9. Marcus Aurelius

Bust of Marcus Aurelius. Vatican Museums, Vatican State.
Courtesy of Alinari/Art Resource, NY.

Marcus Aurelius

Marcus Aurelius, although a philosophically minded thinker, was fated to spend a large part of his reign on the northern frontier, dealing with the Germans. He also suffered from persistent ill-health, and we have the unique advantage of retaining the report of Galen, the doctor who at one critical point, like no doubt others also, looked after him. It is a tenable theory that it was due to his sickness that Marcus Aurelius did not carry out his plan of occupying Germany from the south, a plan which would have greatly affected the whole future course of history, up to the present day.

10. *Commodus*

Bust of Commodus. Vatican Museums, Vatican State.
Courtesy of Alinari/Art Resource, NY.

Commodus

Commodus came to the throne because he was the son of Marcus Aurelius, which proved to be an insufficient reason. Commodus was a bad, cruel, inconsistent emperor, unfit to rule the vast Roman world; he had immediately given up his father's plan to annex Germany. Commodus also had a good deal wrong with him physically, as Galen, who became his doctor, could have told us. And he drank too much. Like other emperors, he was afraid that there would be conspiracies against him—and there were, with eventually fatal results.

11. Septimius Severus

Portrait bust of Septimius Severus. Staatliche Antikensammlung,
Munich, Germany. Courtesy of Alinari/Art Resource, NY.

Septimius Severus

Septimius Severus was an imposing ruler, and whatever the truth about an illness he suffered from in Egypt—it was said to be small-pox, but the existence of small-pox in the Roman empire at that time has been doubted—his feet gave him a great deal of trouble later on in Rome and especially in Britain. The illness has been described as gout, but this too cannot be regarded as certain. In any case, however, the first pains of Septimius Severus probably prevented him from conquering the whole of Scotland.

12. *Caracalla*

Bust of Caracalla. Vatican Museums, Vatican State.
Courtesy of Alinari/Art Resource, NY.

Caracalla

Caracalla was habitually bad-tempered, and there is good reason to believe that he suffered from some physical complaint. This is confirmed by the prominence which his coinage gives to the god of medicine (Aesculapius, Asclepius), whose principal shrine Caracalla visited at Pergamum (Bergama). It used to be thought that Caracalla introduced syphilis to Rome, having brought it back from the east, but that view has now been discarded. Nevertheless there clearly was something wrong with him.

13. Diocletian

Bust of Diocletian. Musei Capitolini, Rome, Italy.
Courtesy of Alinari/Art Resource, NY.

Diocletian

Diocletian's abdication in 305 was the first abdication by an imperial ruler, and was almost certainly caused by ill-health, probably accentuated by weariness after twenty years of imperial rule.

14. Constantine the Great

Constantine, detail of head from full-length statue. S. Giovanni Decollato, Rome, Italy. Courtesy of Alinari/Art Resource, NY.

Constantine the Great

Constantine the Great was told in a dream to fight the Battle of the Milvian Bridge against Maxentius, which resulted in victory and the conquest of Rome. Reliance on the advice 'of the god' in dreams was common in ancient times, and means that we must regard the Greeks and Romans as dedicated to this psychological delusion. It frequently influenced the course of events and must therefore be regarded as among the foremost of the physical, medical causes which prompted them. But this is the best-known and best-recorded instance of an emperor acting in accordance with a dream, and Constantine's action in so doing had an enormous effect on future history.

1. The empire at the death of Augustus

2. Italy and Sicily

3. *Eastern Europe*

4. *North Africa*

5. *The Western Provinces*

antiacum

Danube R.
RAETIA
Vindobona
Carnuntum
Brigetio
PANNONIA
SUPERIOR
Aquincum
Brigantium
NORICUM
PANNONIA
INFERIOR
Drave R. Pelso
Tisza R.
Atrans
Frigidus R.
Emona Siscia
Budalia
Save R.
Sirmium Singidunum
Danube R.
Gamzigrad
Naissus

ITALY

Salona

DALMATIA

Sinuessa

SICILY

MEDITERRANEAN SEA

6. Asia Minor

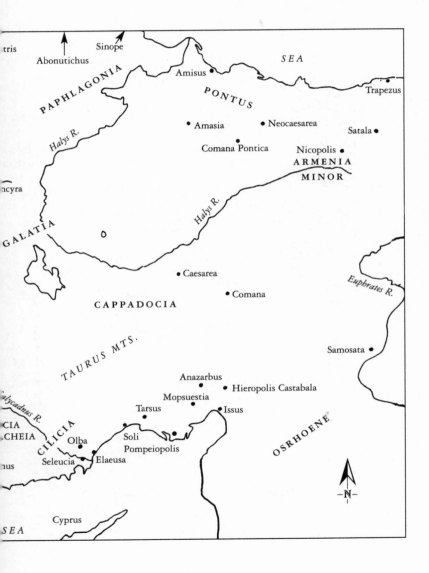

tris

Abonutichus

Sinope

PAPHLAGONIA

SEA

Amisus

PONTUS

Trapezus

cyra

Halys R.

Amasia

Neocaesarea

Satala

Comana Pontica

Nicopolis

ARMENIA
MINOR

GALATIA

Halys R.

Caesarea

Euphrates R.

Comana

CAPPADOCIA

TAURUS MTS.

Samosata

Anazarbus

Hieropolis Castabala

Mopsuestia

alycadnus R.

Tarsus

Issus

CIA
CHEIA

CILICIA

Olba

Soli
Pompeiopolis

OSRHOENE

us

Seleucia

Elaeusa

–N–

Cyprus

SEA

7. *The East*

LATIN *and*
GREEK SOURCES*

A. *Latin*

AUGUSTUS, first emperor, 30 BC–AD 14. Left autobiographical *Res Gestae (Monumentum Ancyranum)*.

CAESAR, dictator, 100–44 BC. Seven books of *Commentaries* on Gallic War (eighth is by Aulus Hirtius), three on *Civil War* (the concluding books on African, Alexandrian and Spanish wars are by other authors).

CATO THE ELDER (Marcus Porcius, 'Censorius'), 234–149 BC. Wrote *De Agri Cultura (c.* 160) and seven books of *Origines,* up to 149 BC.

FRONTO (Marcus Cornelius), *c.* AD 100–*c.* 166. Correspondence with the emperor Marcus Aurelius. Well-known orator.

HADRIAN (Publius Aelius Hadrianus), emperor AD 117–38. Died with versified farewell to his soul on his lips.

HISTORIA AUGUSTA. Collection of biographies of Roman emperors. Of late Roman date. To be taken with a pinch of salt. Prosenatorial.

*Reference to modern works is to be found in the Notes

SCRIPTORES HISTORIAE AUGUSTAE. See *Historia Augusta*.

SUETONIUS (Gaius Suetonius Tranquillus), *c.* AD 69–104 (?), probably from Hippo Regius (Annaba in Algeria). Writings include, especially, *Biographies*.

TACITUS (Publius Cornelius), *c.* AD 56–before or after 117. Probably of Gallic or north Italian origin. Wrote *Agricola, Germania, Dialogue on Orators,* and *Annals,* AD 14–68: out of 18 or 16 books, 10 (minus parts of 3) survive.

TERTULLIAN (Quintus Septimius Florens Tertullianus), *c.* AD 160–*c.* 240. Christian writer. Thirty-one of his works survive.

B. Greek

APPIAN, second century AD. Probably born at Alexandria. History of Roman conquests to Trajan, in 24 books of which 6–9 (mostly) and 11–17 survive.

ARTEMIDORUS of Ephesus (usually known as 'Daldianus', after his mother's native city Daldis in Lydia). Late second century AD. Wrote a number of works including a famous treatise on dreams, *Oneirocritica*.

AURELIUS, MARCUS, see Marcus Aurelius.

CHRISTIANITY. Many writings, of which the best known is the collection in the *New Testament*.

DIO CASSIUS (Cassius Dio Cocceianus), *c.* AD 155–235. From Nicaea (Iznik). Roman History to AD 229, in 80 books of which 36–54 (68–10 BC) are preserved, 55–60 (91 BC–AD 46) exist in abbreviated form, 17 and 70–80 in part. Epitomes of the eleventh and twelfth centuries exist.

GALEN, AD 129–99(?) or later. From Pergamum (Bergama). Rose from gladiator-physician in Asia Minor to court-physician in the Rome of Marcus Aurelius, whom he treated. Voluminous writer on philosophy, anatomy and physiology. His philosophical works are lost, but a good deal of his medical work survives. Enormously influential.

JOSEPHUS (Flavius), born AD 37–38. Wrote *Bellum Judaicum* in seven books (75–79), *Antiquitates Judaicae* in twenty books (93–94), *Vita* and *Contra Apionem* in two books. Jewish priest of aristocratic descent, but settled in Rome under the Flavians.

JULIAN ('Julian the Apostate', Flavius Claudius), emperor 363–64. Published the *Misopogon,* a satirical defence of his actions, and other works, including eight speeches and about eighty letters.

MANILIUS (Marcus), lived under Augustus and Tiberius. Wrote *Astronomica,* a didactic poem on astrology, of which five books are extant.

MARCUS AURELIUS, emperor AD 161–80. Wrote letters to Fronto and philosophical *Meditations.*

PHILO (usually known as Philo Judaeus: *c.* 30 BC–AD 45). Wrote *In Flaccum* and *Legatio ad Gaium* (Caligula). Head of Jewish community at Alexandria.

PLUTARCH (Lucius Mestrius Plutarchus). From Chaeronea. Before AD 50–after 129. Numerous writings include 23 pairs of 'parallel lives' of Greeks and Romans, and Lives of the Caesars (of which only *Galba* and *Otho* survive).

INDEX